はしがき

　物事を成就させるためには、その過程こそが大切です。『seek next 英語総合問題 SECOND EDITION』シリーズは、日頃の基礎固めの英語学習から、さらに受験に対応する力までを養成するために編集された総合問題集です。当シリーズは、各学習段階に応じた5冊から成り、「文法・語法」「作文」「リスニング」「速読」「長文読解」を中心とした構成となっています。

　このシリーズの5冊目にあたる本書『seek next 5 SECOND EDITION』は、全体の総仕上げの位置付けで、大学入試をはじめとしたさまざまな英語の試験に対応できる、即戦的な総合英語力がつくよう編集しています。

　また、各レッスンの「リスニング」と「速読」では、「長文読解」と同じテーマや、関連したテーマの英文を収録しています。リスニングや掲示、記事、Eメールなどのさまざまな読み物を通して、「長文読解」の題材に関する知識を深めることができるようにしています

JN102709

本書の構成と特色

各レッスンは4ページ構成で、全部で15レッスンから成っています。各レッスンを「文法・語法」➡「作文」➡「リスニング」➡「速読」➡「長文読解」の流れで構成しました。

■ Grammar & Usage
●入試頻出の文法・語法項目を問う問題を選択し、入試実践編にふさわしく、各問をアトランダムに配しました。

■ Writing
●整序作文問題もしくは作文問題です。

■ Listening
●各レッスンの「長文読解」と同じテーマの英文を聞き取ります。
●さまざまな試験の形式に対応した問題を収録しています。
● (🔊) は、教師用付属の音声CDのトラック番号を示します。二次元コードを読み取って、音声をPCやスマートフォンなどから聞くこともできます。

■ Rapid Reading
●各レッスンの「長文読解」と同じテーマの英文を収録しています。
●ふつうの英文だけでなく、掲示、記事、Eメールなどの読み取り問題やグラフ問題など、さまざまな形式の問題を収録しています。

■ Reading
●長文読解問題です。興味を引く題材、知的好奇心を喚起する題材、SDGs に対応した題材を選びました。
●各レッスンの「リスニング」と「速読」と同じテーマの英文を収録しています。
●速読問題：設定された時間内に本文を読み、本文の要旨や概要についての理解を問う問題としました。
●精読問題：本文の内容上の重要箇所に関する問題や、本文全体に関する内容把握問題から成ります。

CAN-DO List

●各レッスンの学習の到達目標を「知識・技能」、「思考力・判断力・表現力」の観点から示しています。満点が取れたら、□にチェックを入れましょう。

Contents

Rapid Reading		Reading		
テーマ	問題形式			
幸運	英検®	ある男性に訪れた幸運。		341 words
食品廃棄		食品廃棄について。	1 NO POVERTY / 2 ZERO HUNGER / 12 RESPONSIBLE CONSUMPTION AND PRODUCTION	404 words
伝記		自分の尊敬する人物2人について発表。	1 NO POVERTY / 15 LIFE ON LAND	353 words
ユニバーサルデザイン	英検®	ユニバーサルデザインの原則。	10 REDUCED INEQUALITIES / 11 SUSTAINABLE CITIES AND COMMUNITIES	408 words
集団行動		アリの習性から考える、ものの考え方。		356 words
地球温暖化	共通テスト	地球温暖化について。	13 CLIMATE ACTION	408 words
ストレス	共通テスト	ストレスとその解消に関する統計。	3 GOOD HEALTH AND WELL-BEING	407 words
労働		女性計算手たちの戦い。	5 GENDER EQUALITY / 10 REDUCED INEQUALITIES	418 words
水問題	英検®	増大する水の需要。	2 ZERO HUNGER / 3 GOOD HEALTH AND WELL-BEING / 6 CLEAN WATER AND SANITATION	519 words
社会福祉	英検®	盲導犬について。	11 SUSTAINABLE CITIES AND COMMUNITIES	435 words
人口		人口密度の高い都市部での生き方。	11 SUSTAINABLE CITIES AND COMMUNITIES	460 words
生物	GTEC®	ミツバチの減少。	15 LIFE ON LAND	490 words
求人	GTEC®	コーヒーチェーンの従業員教育。	8 DECENT WORK AND ECONOMIC GROWTH	503 words
心理	英検®	選択肢の多寡が与える心理的影響。		521 words
社会の変化		変化に対応するということ。		524 words

Grammar & Usage   目標➡7分

1 次の各文の ☐ に入れるのに最も適当なものを選びなさい。   （各2点）

1. The post office ☐ last night, but only a small sum of money was taken.   〈日本大〉
   a. has robbed   b. stole   c. was robbed   d. was stolen

2. My application for the loan didn't ☐ the bank's requirements.   〈学習院大〉
   a. break   b. get   c. meet   d. raise

3. Jane works part-time as a pianist at a restaurant, and she ☐ 500 dollars a week.
   a. earns   b. wins   c. catches   d. profits

4. You'd better ☐ your English before you go to Los Angeles this summer.   〈上智大〉
   a. brush up   b. curl in   c. cut out   d. sharpen off

5. I find it difficult to get up early in the morning, so I have to ☐ breakfast.
   a. do without   b. get rid of   c. put up with   d. slow down

6. We've run ☐ of milk. Could you go and buy some at the supermarket?〈学習院大〉
   a. down   b. out   c. over   d. up

7. He is very friendly. He can get ☐ anybody.   〈法政大〉
   a. through with   b. with together   c. out of   d. along with

8. A : We had terrible weather during our vacation.   B : ☐? What a shame!
   a. Did you   b. Had it   c. Was it   d. Were you

9. A : Do you mind my dropping by tomorrow afternoon?   B : ☐   〈東海大〉
   a. I hope so.   b. Of course not.   c. No, I do.   d. Mind you.

Writing   目標➡3分

2 1、2は（ ）内の語句を並べかえなさい。3、4は英訳しなさい。   （1、2：各3点／3、4：各6点）

1. 一日でどのくらい遠くまで行けると思いますか。   〈青山学院大〉
   (you / can / go / we / think / far / do / how) in a day?

   _____

2. Before I went to the U.S., I had (would be like / what / it / no idea / to live) in a foreign country.

   _____

3. スミス先生はどんな質問をすると思いますか。   〈福岡女子大〉

   _____

4. 10年後の東京はどのようになっているのだろうか。   〈青山学院大〉

   _____

CAN-DO List ☐ 🔍 〈知識・技能〉ランダムに配列された文法・語法に関する問題に答えることができる。

Listening 目標➡5分

3 それぞれの写真について4つの説明が読まれます。写真に最も合っているものを一つずつ選びなさい。 (各5点)

1.

① ② ③ ④

2.

① ② ③ ④

Rapid Reading 目標➡5分

テーマ 幸運 英検®

4 (1)・(2)に入れるのに最も適当なものを一つずつ選びなさい。 (各5点)

It was a normal weekend day until noon. Uncle Bob and Aunt Mimi went shopping at a nearby mall, and I mowed the lawn. At 12:15, they returned, and we sat down to lunch. Uncle Bob was commenting on how nice the grass looked when suddenly the phone rang. It was the lottery commission, calling to tell Uncle Bob that he held the winning ticket. Not ten minutes later, the phone began ringing continually. First a news reporter called. Almost immediately after that, it was a news network. During the afternoon, an army of reporters came and went. Uncle Bob said that he needed to get some fresh air and (1). Upon opening the door, however, he got a big shock. Hundreds of people stood in the street in front of the house, hoping to get a look at (2).

1. ① buy lottery tickets
   ② have a good sleep
   ③ make his apologies
   ④ take a walk
2. ① the country's funniest comedian
   ② the country's most popular news reporter
   ③ the country's most successful businessman
   ④ the country's newest millionaire

Reading 目標➡20分 //////////////////////////////////// テーマ 幸運 ((◀)) 4

速読問題 次の英文を2分で読んで、1. の問いに答えなさい。

A woman was walking along the Thames River in London one day late in June 1937. Suddenly, she threw a bottle into the calm water. It was a whiskey bottle. Its cap was closed very tightly. The bottle contained no liquid, just a note. Then she turned and left.

That same bottle was found on March 16, 1949, on a beach near San Francisco. (1)12 years is
5 a long time for a bottle to float on the sea, but a scientist later calculated (2)the route the bottle followed.

First, the bottle traveled into *the Straits of Dover and onward to the North Sea. After that, it crossed the North Atlantic. (3)Hundreds and hundreds of kilometers of Norwegian coast were likely seen by the bottle. The brave bottle then made its way through the Barents Sea,
10 just north of Russia. Then out into the East Siberian Sea it sailed. Finally, across the Bering Sea and down the long western coast of the United States the little bottle went, until its 20,000 km trip came to an end on (4)that California beach.

Now back to March 16, 1949. The little bottle had not been broken during its journey. (5)However, the spirit of Jack Wurm, a 55-year-old man with no job, was broken.
15 His restaurant had gone out of business. Jack had no money.

Jack saw the whiskey bottle while walking on the beach that day. There was something inside of it. He couldn't get the cap off, so he broke the glass on some rocks. Inside of the bottle, he found (6)this: "I don't want any confusion. I'm leaving all of my money to the lucky person who finds this bottle. However, you must share it, half of it, with Barry Cohen, my
20 lawyer. Daisy Alexander, June 20, 1937."

Daisy Alexander was a lovable, strange old woman who died in 1939 with no family. Her ancestors, however, had started and developed *the Singer Sewing Company.

Jack picked up a bottle ... and $6,000,000 at the same time. The other $6,000,000 was given to her lawyer.

(341 words / 大阪産業大)

CAN-DO List □ 📖 〈思考力・判断力・表現力〉「幸運」をテーマとしたストーリーの展開を的確に理解することができる。

⁷the Straits of Dover：ドーバー海峡　　²²the Singer Sewing Company：シンガー（ミシン製造会社）

1. この英文のタイトルとして最も適当なものを選びなさい。　　　　　　　　　　　　　　（5点）

　　a．A Bottle's 12-year Journey on the Seas

　　b．A Lucky Man Who Picked Up $6,000,000

　　c．A Rich Woman Who Died with No Family

　　d．The Route a Bottle Followed

精 読問題 もう一度英文を読んで、次の問いに答えなさい。

2. 下線部(1)を参考にして、次の日本文の意味を表す英文を完成しなさい。　　　　　　　（3点）

　　2マイルは、子供が歩くには長い道のりです。

　　Two miles（a child / a long way / for / is / to / walk）.

　　_____

3. 下線部(2)の具体的な内容になるように、下線部に語句を補いなさい。　　　　　　　　（3点）

　　The route between _____ and _____.

4. 下線部(3)とほぼ同じ意味になるように、（　　）内に適語を補いなさい。　　　　　　（3点）

　　Probably the bottle（　　　　　　）up（　　　　　　）hundreds and hundreds of kilometers of Norwegian coast.

5. 下線部(4)の具体的な内容を表す語句を抜き出しなさい。　　　　　　　　　　　　　　（5点）

　　_____

6. 下線部(5)は何と何とを「しかしながら」と結びつけているか。日本語で説明しなさい。　（5点）

　　_____

7. 下線部(6)の具体的な内容を、70字程度の日本語で説明しなさい。　　　　　　　　　（10点）

　　　　　　　　　　　　　　　　　　　　70

8. 全体把握 本文の内容と合っているものをすべて選びなさい。　　　　　　　　　　　（10点）

　　a．It took nearly 12 years for the bottle to reach California.

　　b．The bottle crossed the Pacific Ocean.

　　c．The straight-line distance between London and San Francisco is 20,000 km.

　　d．Jack had failed in the restaurant business.

　　e．Jack received all of Daisy's fortune.

　　f．Daisy's note was written 10 years before her death.

Lesson 2

Grammar & Usage　目標→7分

1 次の会話の ☐ に入れるのに最も適当なものを選びなさい。　　　　　　　　（各2点）

1. A : If it's a nice day tomorrow, what do you say about going for a picnic?
   B : I'd like that, but the weather report ☐ it's going to rain.　　〈上智大〉
   a. prophesies　　　b. will predict　　　c. says　　　d. probably thinks

2. A : You are coming with us to the beach on Sunday, aren't you?
   B : I'm really sorry, but I won't be able to ☐ it after all.
   a. give　　　b. make　　　c. miss　　　d. save

3. A : You won't believe this but I just won the lottery——$10 million!
   B : You're ☐ !　Ten million dollars?!　　〈上智大〉
   a. kissing　　　b. filling　　　c. kidding　　　d. chilling

2 次の各組の文がほぼ同じ意味になるように、（　）内に適語を補いなさい。　（各3点）

1. They provided the homeless with blankets.
   They provided blankets (　　　　　) the homeless.　　〈立教大〉

2. It is impossible to know what she will do next.
   There is (　　　　) (　　　　　　) what she will do next.　　〈福島大〉

3. They got married seven years ago.
   Seven years (　　　　) (　　　　　) since they got married.　　〈小樽商科大〉

4. I could not go out because of the rain.
   The rain (　　　　) me (　　　　　) going out.　　〈福島大〉

Writing　目標→3分

3 1、2は（　）内の語句を並べかえなさい。3、4は英訳しなさい。　（1、2：各3点／3、4：各6点）

1. あなたのドレスにその靴はまったく合いません。（1語不要）　　〈中央大〉
   (not / those / your dress / go / shoes / do / with / at all / come).

2. 男の子たちにからかわれたので、彼は頭にきている。（1語不要）　　〈福島大〉
   He is (ill / because / making / some / upset / boys / him / of / were / fun).

3. その単語の意味がわからなかったので、辞書で調べてみました。　　〈学習院大〉
   As I didn't know what ＿＿＿＿＿＿＿＿＿＿＿＿＿＿＿＿＿＿＿＿ in a dictionary.

4. 彼は空港に着いたらすぐきみに電話すると言っていた。　　〈学習院大〉
   He said ＿＿＿＿＿＿＿＿＿＿＿＿＿＿＿＿＿＿＿＿＿＿＿＿＿.

4 対話と質問を聞き、その答えとして最も適当なものを一つずつ選びなさい。　　　（各5点）

1. ① A fishing rod.
   ③ An antivirus software.
   ② A milk bottle.
   ④ Coffee beans.

2. ① About cooking beans.
   ③ About food waste.
   ② About food processing.
   ④ About the importance of trying his best.

Rapid Reading

目標➡5分　　　　　　　　　　　　　　　　　テーマ 食品廃棄

5 ポスターを読み取って、問いに対する答えとして最も適当なものを一つずつ選びなさい。　　（各5点）

Food Loss (FL) takes place at ...	Food Waste (FW) happens at ...
Agricultural Production & Harvest ⇒At the farm: If they produce too many products, they have to throw them away to adjust to the lower demand. **Processing Stages** ⇒ At the factory: When the shapes or colors of the products are different from the standard ones, they are thrown away. **Distribution** ⇒Some products are damaged during their transportation. In developing countries, 40 percent of losses happen before food even reaches the market. We need to improve how food is stored, processed and distributed.	**Retail & Consumption** ⇒Restaurants & Catering Customers order more than they need. Foods are discarded before served. They have huge amounts of buffet table leftovers and plate leftovers. ⇒Domestic Consumption About two-thirds of food waste at home is due to food not being used before it goes bad. ⇒Supermarkets & Stores Supermarkets in the U. S. lose $15 billion annually in unsold fruit and vegetables alone.

How can we help reduce FW?　Our behavior can change the situation!

1. Ask for smaller portions: Don't order more food than you can eat.
2. Buy "ugly" fruit and vegetables: Even if the shapes or colors do not look good or look funny, their taste does not change.
3. Love your leftovers: No leftovers lead to reducing FW. If they are still edible, you can get a to-go box, a doggy bag, or bring your own container.
4. Mobile apps and social media: They can also be used to minimize FW. Some apps offer the information on discounted products with a best-before date.

1. What are the differences between FL and FW?
   ① FL is to throw away agricultural products and FW is to throw away leftovers of restaurants.
   ② FL occurs after the food is delivered to the consumers, while FW takes place among the farmers.
   ③ FL occurs among the food suppliers while FW happens among the food retailers and consumers.
   ④ FL occurs mainly in restaurants and transport companies, while FW happens on farms and in households.

2. According to the poster, what can we do to prevent FW as consumers?
   ① Get information about FW through mobile apps and buy appropriate food to reduce FW.
   ② Get information about the differences between FL and FW and make presentations about them.
   ③ Harvest "ugly" fruit and vegetables and distribute them to each household.
   ④ Leave leftovers at restaurants so that other people can enjoy them.

Reading 目標→20分 ・・・・・・・・・・・・・・・ テーマ 食品廃棄 7

速読問題 次の英文を2.5分で読んで、1. の問いに答えなさい。

(1)Legislation calling for greater efforts to curb the waste of edible food——at every stage from production to consumption——has been enacted by the Diet. It requires the national government to (2)come up with a basic policy to (3)address the "food loss" problem and makes it (4)mandatory for local governments to (5)craft specific plans of action. While the problem of
5 overproduction and sales is often highlighted in discussing the issue, consumers can play a significant role in reducing such waste by changing their own behavior.

The government estimates that of the 27.59 million tons of food wasted in this country in fiscal 2016, food still fit for consumption amounted to (6)6.43 million tons——a volume that has remained roughly unchanged for the past several years. That is equivalent to each person in
10 Japan throwing away one rice bowl of food every day —— roughly double the annual worldwide food aid distributed to poor countries suffering from food shortage.

Food waste is an increasingly serious problem worldwide. Roughly 1.3 billion tons of food is reportedly wasted globally each year——even as more than 800 million people worldwide continue to suffer from malnutrition. (7)The UN Sustainable Development Goals (SDGs) call
15 for halving per capita food waste by 2030. Overproduction of food and the disposal of food also result in wasteful energy consumption and the discharge of gases that contribute to global warming. Cutting back on food waste is a particularly serious challenge for Japan since it relies heavily on imports to meet its food demand.

In recent years, the problem of food waste has often been highlighted as an issue of mass
20 production and sales——and the subsequent disposal of unsold products——of food linked to specific events or days on the calendar such as "lucky" sushi rolls to be eaten on Setsubun in February or Christmas cakes. In January, the government took the unusual step of asking supermarket and convenience store chain operators to make and sell just enough eho-maki sushi rolls to meet consumer demand to avoid a large-scale disposal of unsold rolls. (8)Major
25 convenience store chain operators have meanwhile indicated that they will start allowing their franchise stores to sell boxed lunches and other food nearing the end of their shelf lives effectively at discount prices to cut back on the disposal of those food products——the cost of which is largely borne by the franchisees.

(404 words／青山学院大)

CAN-DO List □ 〈思考力・判断力・表現力〉「食料問題」をテーマとした英文の展開を的確に理解することができる。

1. この英文は全体として何について述べているか。一つ選びなさい。 （5点）

   a. Consumers solving problems of food production

   b. Food loss due to overproduction

   c. The Diet making policies for food waste

   d. Wasted "lucky" sushi rolls on Setsubun

精 読問題 もう一度英文を読んで、次の問いに答えなさい。

2. 下線部(1)の legislation は何を要求する法律か。日本語で説明しなさい。 （5点）

_____

3. 下線部(2)〜(5)の意味として最も適当なものを一つずつ選びなさい。 （各2点）

   (2) a. catch up with　　b. come across　　c. hit upon　　d. keep up with

   (3) a. deal with　　b. follow　　c. speak to　　d. talk about

   (4) a. apparent　　b. frequent　　c. important　　d. obligatory

   (5) a. boldly make　　b. carefully make　　c. freely make　　d. instantly make

4. 下線部(6)の数字は本文中ではどのように言いかえられているか。空所に日本語を補い、説明を完成しなさい。 （各2点）

   日本にいる人一人当たり[(1) 　　　　　]の食べ物を毎日[(2) 　　　　　]ことに匹敵し、[(3) 　　　　　]に悩む貧困国に提供される世界の年間の[(4) 　　　　　]の２倍である。

5. 下線部(7)の SDGs が2030年までに求めていることは何か。日本語で説明しなさい。 （5点）

_____

6. 下線部(8)について、大手コンビニチェーンの経営陣が、それぞれのフランチャイズ店に許可することは何か。本文の内容に合うものを一つ選びなさい。 （5点）

   a. 消費期限が近づいている弁当やほかの食べ物を割引して販売すること。

   b. 消費期限のある弁当やほかの食べ物を割引せずに廃棄すること。

   c. 弁当などの消費期限が切れた食べ物を割引して販売すること。

   d. 弁当やそのほかの食べ物を消費期限を延長して割引すること。

7. 全体把握 本文の内容と合っているものをすべて選びなさい。 （8点）

   a. Consumers have already been playing a significant role in reducing food waste for many years.

   b. It is reported that, in the world, about 1.3 billion tons of food is thrown away every year.

   c. Overproducing food has resulted from wasteful energy consumption and global warming.

   d. In recent years, it has been thought that the issue of food waste can be solved by the mass production and sales of the food.

   e. Throwing away unsold food products is done on specific events or days on the calendar.

   f. In January, supermarket and convenience store chain operators were asked to make and sell just enough eho-maki sushi rolls to meet consumer demand.

Lesson 3

Grammar & Usage　目標➡7分

1 次の各文の ☐ に入れるのに最も適当なものを選びなさい。　　（各2点）

1. Give me a call when you ☐ your homework.　〈日本女子大〉
   - a. finish
   - b. finished
   - c. will finish
   - d. will have finished

2. Saki, why don't you take some time off?　You ☐ too hard lately.
   - a. would work
   - b. had worked
   - c. should have worked
   - d. have been working

3. I wonder if Stella has lost my number.　☐ her call for the last two hours.
   - a. I'd expected
   - b. I'll have expected
   - c. I'm expecting
   - d. I've been expecting

4. There's no public transportation, so we may ☐ walk to that place.　〈関西学院大〉
   - a. as well
   - b. well to
   - c. well as to
   - d. as well as

5. We had a great time at the party last night.　You ☐ come.　〈上智大〉
   - a. had to
   - b. must have
   - c. might have
   - d. ought to have

6. Here is the pen I promised ☐.　〈関西外国語大〉
   - a. lending you
   - b. to you to lend
   - c. for you to lend
   - d. to lend you

7. This book is well worth ☐.　〈青山学院大〉
   - a. read
   - b. for reading
   - c. in reading
   - d. reading

8. A : I bought this new software program, but I can't ☐ how to use it.
   B : I have the same program.　I'll show you how.　〈上智大〉
   - a. think about
   - b. know of
   - c. figure out
   - d. find about

Writing　目標➡3分

2 1、2は（　）内の語句を並べかえなさい。3、4は英訳しなさい。　（1、2：各3点／3、4：各6点）

1. きみは毎月給料の一部を銀行に預けるべきだったよ。　〈関西外国語大〉
   You (your salary / the bank / should / in / part / have / put / of) each month.

2. きみは彼の誤りを笑うべきではなかった。　〈愛媛大〉
   You (at / his / not / to / ought / error / laughed / have).

3. 昨夜、彼はもう少しで自動車にひかれそうになった。　〈日本女子大〉

4. 日本人はユーモアのセンスがないとよく言われます。　〈鳥取大〉

12　CAN-DO List　☐　〈知識・技能〉ランダムに配列された文法・語法に関する問題に答えることができる。

3 英語の質問と、それに対する応答が4つ読まれます。応答として最も適当なものを一つずつ選び
なさい。 (各5点)

1. ① ② ③ ④　　　　　　　　　2. ① ② ③ ④

Rapid Reading 目標➡5分 テーマ 伝記

4 偉人の伝記を読み取って、問いに対する答えとして最も適当なものを一つずつ選びなさい。(各5点)

1847	Thomas Alva Edison was born in Milan, Ohio on February 11.
1854	The Edison family moved to Port Huron, Michigan.
around 1855	He had school education for only 3 months. It is said that his mother taught him at home.
1871	He married 16-year-old Mary Stilwell.
1876	He moved to a new laboratory at Menlo Park, New Jersey.
1877	He invented the phonograph and sold them for many decades.
1879	He and his team made a light bulb which lasted for more than 13 hours.
1884	Mary Edison died at the age of 29.
1886	He married 20-year-old Mina Miller. They moved into Glenmont in West Orange, New Jersey.
1887	He opened his new laboratory at West Orange, close to his new home.
1892	The War of Currents (DC: direct current power delivery system vs. AC: alternative current power delivery system) came to an end. He had insisted that DC was superior to AC. Edison's company was generating much smaller profits than its AC rivals.
1894	The first public showing of motion pictures took place with the opening of a "peephole" kinetoscope parlor. People started watching movies in theaters on big movie screens.
1896	He met Henry Ford, who worked as an engineer for Edison's company. He encouraged the development of Ford's automobile.
1931	He died at his home, Glenmont, on October 18.
1947	Mina Edison outlived him, dying on August 24, at the age of 82.

1. Which of the following statements is true?

　① Before motion pictures were invented, people had enjoyed watching movies.

　② Edison established his laboratory at Menlo Park, and used it all through his life.

　③ Edison died at the age of 84.

　④ Edison majored in engineering at university.

2. Which of the following statements is best supported by the above timeline?

　① Edison and Henry Ford cooperated with each other.

　② Edison was married only once.

　③ Edison was an inventor, not a businessman.

　④ Edison's company pushed forward with AC.

Reading

速 読問題 次の英文を2分で読んで、1. の問いに答えなさい。

A role model is an ideal person whom we admire. Role models may have various backgrounds and ways of looking at things. However, they all inspire others through their actions. I would like to introduce two people I admire.

Mr. Chico Mendes is one of my role models. He was born in the Amazon region in 1944 to a

5 poor Brazilian family that had farmed rubber from rubber trees for many generations. They loved the rainforest and used (1)its resources in a way that did not destroy it. However, mining companies and cattle ranchers started destroying the Amazon rainforest which is more than 180 million years old. They burned and cut down hundreds of thousands of trees, endangering the living environment of the people there. Chico began a movement that

10 organized ordinary workers to oppose (2)those harmful practices. The movement eventually spread to other parts of the world, as Chico's efforts led people in other countries to protect the earth's forests and the forests' native inhabitants. Mr. Chico Mendes is a role model for me because of his courage, dedication and self-sacrificing work to protect not only the Amazon rainforest, but the natural environment of the entire planet.

15 Dr. Mae Jemison, the first Afro-American female astronaut to travel into space, is my other role model. Mae was born into a middle-class American family. She entered university at the age of 16, and went on to receive degrees in Chemical Engineering, African-American Studies and Medicine. She became a fluent speaker of Japanese, Russian and Swahili. In 1992, she was the science mission specialist on the space shuttle Endeavour, on a cooperative

20 mission between the U.S. and Japan. A compassionate person, (3)Dr. Jemison has used her education to improve the lives of others by providing primary medical care to poor people. She has helped countless people through various educational and medical projects.

The main characteristics of my two role models are that they sympathize with other people's distress and are committed to improving the world by (4)helping others. They are

25 caring people who use their potential to benefit the world, making it a better place.

(353 words)

1. Chico Mendes と Mae Jemison に共通しているものを選びなさい。　　　　　　　（5点）

   a．They devoted themselves to caring for poor people.

   b．They organized a movement for preserving the natural environment.

   c．They sympathized with people in distress and engaged in making a better world.

   d．They were raised in a poor family, but got a good education.

精 読問題 もう一度英文を読んで、次の問いに答えなさい。

2. 下線部(1)の具体的な内容を、英語2語で抜き出しなさい。　　　　　　　　　（4点）

   (　　　　　　　)（　　　　　　　）

3. 下線部(2)の具体的な内容を、日本語で説明しなさい。　　　　　　　　　　　（8点）

_____

_____

4. 下線部(3)の行動は、ジェミソンさんのどのような性格によるものか。形容詞1語で抜き出しなさい。

   (　　　　　　　)　　　　　　　　　　　　　　　　　　　　　　　　　　（3点）

5. 下線部(4)について、メンデスさんとジェミソンさんが助けたのはどのような人々か。それぞれ日本語で説明しなさい。　　　　　　　　　　　　　　　　　　　　　　　（各4点）

   メンデスさん：_____

   ジェミソンさん：_____

6. 全体把握 ［　　　］に入れるのに最も適当なものを一つずつ選びなさい。　（各6点）

  ⑴ Chico's family loved the rainforest and ［　　　］.

    a．did not tell outsiders the location of their rubber trees

    b．did not want strangers to live anywhere near them

    c．protected the native people from being killed

    d．took good care of their rubber trees

  ⑵ Chico's movement to protect the Amazon rainforest and the people living there ［　　　］.

    a．became a world-wide movement

    b．remained basically a problem for Brazilian people

    c．was especially concerned with global warming

    d．was focused mainly on the Amazon rubber trees

  ⑶ Dr. Jemison devoted herself to improving the lives of others because ［　　　］.

    a．she loved traveling as a tourist

    b．she wanted to gain experience as a doctor

    c．she wanted an adventure

    d．she was a caring person

Grammar & Usage   目標➡7分

1 次の会話の □ に入れるのに最も適当なものを選びなさい。   （各4点）

1. *A :* There are many things you could do to improve your health.

   B : □

   A : Getting regular exercise, for example, or eating more vegetables.

   a. Any similar examples?   b. How many?

   c. Like what?   d. What did you say?

2. *A :* Brain Ford is the man for the job, don't you think?

   B : □

   A : Who do you suggest, then?

   a. I'm afraid I don't agree.   b. I'm sorry, I didn't hear you.

   c. In my opinion, you're right.   d. That's exactly what I think.

3. *A :* I'm from Edinburgh in Scotland.

   B : Really? I spent a couple of weeks in Britain last year, but didn't have a chance to visit Edinburgh. □

   A : It's a beautiful city, but the wind can be quite cold!

   a. How about it?   b. What's it like?

   c. Can you tell it to me?   d. Do you know it?

4. *A :* I don't feel well at all. I've got an awful headache.

   B : Why don't you take a □ off today? I'll call your office and tell them you're not coming in.

   a. day   b. holiday   c. rest   d. work

Writing   目標➡3分

2 1、2は（　　）内の語を並べかえなさい。3、4は英訳しなさい。   （1、2：各3点／3、4：各6点）

1. Several of those who (accident / been / have / survived / taken / the) to hospital in a state of shock.   〈立教大〉

2. 結婚する相手のことはできるだけ知らないほうがいいのかもしれない。   〈立命館大〉

   It (little / as / be / to / may / better / know) as possible about the person you're going to marry.

3. 人間は生きるために道具を使わなければならない。   〈日本女子大〉

4. そんな危ないことをするなんて、彼はおろかだった。   〈日本女子大〉

Listening

目標➡ 5分　　テーマ ユニバーサルデザイン　GTEC®　 11〜12

3 英語の質問と、それに対する応答が4つ読まれます。応答として最も適当なものを一つずつ選びなさい。　　　(各5点)

1. ① ②. ③ ④　　　　　　　　　2. ① ② ③ ④

Rapid Reading

目標➡ 5分　　テーマ ユニバーサルデザイン　英検®

4 Eメールを読んで、問いに対する答えとして最も適当なものを一つずつ選びなさい。　(各5点)

From: Daniel Ho <daniel.ho@lillyput.ne.uk>
To: Hotel Manager <reservation@theparkinthesky.co.uk>
Date: January 14
Subject: Need Special Assistance

Dear Hotel Manager,

　I have an upcoming booking at your hotel and am looking forward to staying there. Unfortunately, however, I have to inform you that I sprained my ankle last week and am having some difficulty walking around. In fact, I will have to use a wheelchair during the stay. Before my stay from January 24 to 27, I would appreciate it if you could tell me about the accessibility of your hotel. Specifically, I would like to check the following items.

1. Step-free access to the ground floor entrance of the hotel with wide automatic doors
2. Ground level reception / check-in desk
3. Lift access to my floor
4. Shower chair in the bathroom
5. Toilet with grab rails
6. Towels and other bathroom supplies placed at an accessible height
7. Turning room for a wheelchair on each side of the bed, and in the bathroom

　This is the very first time that I must use a wheelchair for going out. I am a bit worried about my stay at your hotel. I am sorry to bother you, but please understand my situation. I would be thankful if your hotel offers facilities based on the principles of Universal Design.

　Sincerely,

　Daniel Ho

1. Why has Daniel sent an e-mail to the hotel manager?
   ① He has gotten injured and needs special assistance from other people.
   ② He has sprained his wrist, so he needs to check the hotel facilities and accessibility.
   ③ He needs to check the hotel location because he has some difficulty moving around.
   ④ He needs to use his wheelchair and know a lot about the hotel.

2. What does Daniel need during his stay?
   ① He needs an extra room at the hotel entrance so he can turn his wheelchair around.
   ② He needs every assist provided by the hotel staff.
   ③ He needs handrails for every facility that he is going to use.
   ④ He needs hotel facilities that are suitable for using his wheelchair.

CAN-DO List　☐ 🎧 〈思考力・判断力・表現力〉不意の問いかけに対する適当な応答を判断できる。
　　　　　　☐ 📖 〈思考力・判断力・表現力〉Eメールを読んで概要を把握することができる。

Reading

目標➡20分　　　　　　テーマ　ユニバーサルデザイン　🔊 13

速 読問題 次の英文を2.5分で読んで、1. の問いに答えなさい。

(1)The Seven Principles on Universal Design (UD) were developed by a group of architects, product designers, engineers and environmental design researchers. The purpose of the principles is to guide the design of living and working spaces, products, and methods of communication that benefit the widest possible range of people.

5　Designing a product or a living/working environment involves aesthetics, engineering options, environmental issues, safety concerns, industry standards, and cost. Usually, designers focus on the average user but UD aims to also include the non-standard user.

The details of all seven principles cannot be fully explained in a short article such as this. Instead, a general idea of their application can be seen in examples of the principles in action.

10　First, there are (2)many examples that already are common features in modern society. In cities, there are special bricks in the sidewalk that have bumps and form a path that a blind person can follow. At crosswalks, there may be audible signals for those who are blind. Accommodations for the people with disabilities include special access toilets, installation of ramps, and elevators that speak and have buttons within reach of a person in a wheelchair.

15　(3)Universal Design also aims to include, not just those with disabilities, but other people outside of the average and, of course, within the average. It considers, for example, the needs of very tall or short people, both left handed and right handed people, tourists who don't speak the local language and people who have special needs. When you see a sign that explains how to use a machine with writing and images, it is an example of Universal Design principles
20　in action.

A selection of words used to explain the seven principles may show, in general, how they work. "Flexibility, Simplicity, Low Effort, Choice, Adaptability, Compatibility, and Safety" are some of the goals outlined in the principles. UD can be applied to any product or environment, such as tutoring and learning centers, conference exhibits, museums,
25　recreational areas, homes and worksites.

There are critics of UD that point out the contradiction of trying to meet individual, unique needs at the same time you want to cover the needs of the average user. They say that the guidelines in UD are too vague. However, improvements to the principles are taking place to answer (4)the critics. If you have ever been in a situation where you have had a disability,
30　either a temporarily broken arm or leg, or a long-term disability, you may be thankful that thoughtful designers are using the principles of Universal Design.　　　　(408 words / 摂南大)

1. この英文は全体として何について述べているか。一つ選びなさい。 （5点）

  a. UD as a general idea of how to deal with people who need help from others

  b. UD as a guideline for designing a product or a living or working environment

  c. UD in an environment where designers can contribute to social welfare

  d. UD in special accommodations for tourists who don't speak the local language

精 読問題 もう一度英文を読んで、次の問いに答えなさい。

2. 下線部(1)の目的は何か。70字程度の日本語で説明しなさい。 （6点）

（70字のマス目）

3. 第2パラグラフの内容と一致するものを一つ選びなさい。 （5点）

  a. Designers usually do not care about the cost of making products.

  b. Industrial standards are the most important factor in designing products.

  c. Many factors are taken into consideration in designing living or working environments.

  d. UD gives the highest priority to non-standard users.

4. 下線部(2)に関して挙げられている街中での例と横断歩道での例について、日本語で説明しなさい。

（各5点）

街中で：＿＿＿＿＿＿＿＿＿＿＿＿＿＿＿＿＿＿＿＿＿＿＿＿＿＿＿＿＿＿

横断歩道で：＿＿＿＿＿＿＿＿＿＿＿＿＿＿＿＿＿＿＿＿＿＿＿＿＿＿

5. 下線部(3)について、本文の内容に合うものを一つ選びなさい。 （5点）

  a. UD can meet the demand of average people, as well as people with disabilities or who are outside the average.

  b. UD cannot satisfy the needs of tall or short people and both left handed and right handed people.

  c. UD will not accept the needs of people with disabilities but rather of those who are average or above average.

  d. UD will deny not only what people with disabilities need but also what others require.

6. 下線部(4)の critics による批判はどのようなものか。日本語で説明しなさい。 （7点）

＿＿＿＿＿＿＿＿＿＿＿＿＿＿＿＿＿＿＿＿＿＿＿＿＿＿＿＿＿＿

7. **全体把握** 本文の内容と合っているものをすべて選びなさい。 （8点）

  a. UD is a guideline for designing a product or a living/working environment that fits the largest range of people.

  b. One example of UD principles is the instructions with words and images about how to use a machine.

  c. UD pays attention to non-standard users only.

  d. The UD principles contain "Flexibility, Simplicity, Low Effort, Choice, Adaptability, Compatibility, and Safety" as their sales points.

  e. Some critics say that UD should prepare vague guidelines so that everyone can have access to UD products.

Lesson 5

Grammar & Usage　目標➡5分

1 次の各文の下線部とほぼ同じ意味を表すものを選びなさい。　　　　　　　　（各3点）

1. We were all <u>taken in</u> by his good manners and polished way of talking.　〈成蹊大〉
   a. deceived　　　　b. encouraged　　　c. pleased　　　　d. impressed

2. I didn't understand what he <u>was driving at</u>.　〈立命館大〉
   a. meant　　　　　b. feared　　　　　c. confessed　　　d. sent

3. In order to build the highway, they had to <u>tear down</u> that whole block of buildings.
   a. cover up　　　　b. pull down　　　c. move　　　　　d. rebuild　〈成城大〉

4. She <u>took on</u> too much for one so young.　〈立命館大〉
   a. tried to do　　　b. found out　　　c. grew up　　　　d. brought on

2 次の各文の下線部のうちから誤りを含むものを一つずつ選びなさい。　　　　（各3点）

1. The value _{a.}<u>of the yen</u> _{b.}<u>declines</u> _{c.}<u>as</u> the rate of inflation _{d.}<u>raises</u>.　〈早稲田大〉

2. _{a.}<u>No matter how</u> difficult _{b.}<u>the problem is</u>, you should never _{c.}<u>give up it</u> _{d.}<u>until the last moment</u>.　〈青山学院大〉

3. _{a.}<u>How clever</u> _{b.}<u>for you</u> _{c.}<u>to buy</u> chocolate chip _{d.}<u>cookies</u> — they are my favorite!

4. I'll never forget _{a.}<u>to get</u> lost _{b.}<u>when</u> we _{c.}<u>were climbing in</u> _{d.}<u>the</u> Alps last year.〈日本大〉

Writing　目標➡5分

3 1〜3は（　　）内の語句を並べかえなさい。4、5は英訳しなさい。　（1〜3：各3点／4、5：各6点）

1. She's only crying because she wants (feel / for / her / sorry / to / you).　Ignore her and she'll stop.

   _____

2. It is not how much you read (but / counts / read / that / what / you).

   _____

3. テレビ放送を実現するには多くの年月と多くのさまざまな人を要した。
   It took many years and (make / many different people / television / to / work).

   _____

4. 私の母は忘れっぽい人だった。ある日、スリッパをはいたまま仕事に出かけてしまった。
   My mother was an absent-minded person.　One day, _____.

5. また別の買い物袋をもらって紙を浪費しないように、私は買い物袋をいつも持参している。
   I always take a shopping bag with me so _____.

4 対話を聞き、問いの答えとして最も適当なものを一つずつ選びなさい。 （各5点）

状況

英語の授業で、パソコンで情報を検索しながら、Rika と Koji が話しています。

1. What article does Rika want Koji to know about?
   ① About communication between ants.
   ② About how sympathetic ants are to other ants.
   ③ About how to keep ants for a long time.
   ④ About nonverbal communication made between humans.

2. What has Koji known about before the conversation?
   ① Ants' ways of communication.
   ② The metamorphosis of ants.
   ③ The structures of ant holes.
   ④ Scented chemicals produced by ants.

Rapid Reading 目標➡5分 　テーマ 集団行動

5 英文を読んで、問いに対する答えとして最も適当なものを一つずつ選びなさい。 （各5点）

　Group discussion is a face-to-face meeting among a small number of people.　Generally, the purpose of such meetings is to convey information, express views, and reach conclusions. How well you can communicate within a group will affect the quality of decisions your group makes.　The more effectively you and the other group members communicate, the more informed your decisions are likely to be.　Two important parts of effective communication are knowing how to analyze problems and how to reach decisions with which everyone can agree. When you study group discussion, you will learn formal methods of problem-solving and decision-making.　These methods will help you to be an active and productive participant in whatever kinds of discussions you choose to join.

1. Which of the following statements is NOT true?
   ① It is important to reach some decisions even if not everyone can agree with them.
   ② One of the purposes of group discussion is to reach conclusions about a matter.
   ③ Problem-solving and decision-making are purposes of group discussions.
   ④ The quality of decisions will be affected by how well people can communicate within a group.

2. According to the article, who is the best participant in a group discussion?
   ① A person who is always critical of the opinions of other participants.
   ② A person who is familiar with psychology.
   ③ A person who is fluent in various languages.
   ④ A person who makes a lot of communication with other participants.

CAN-DO List  □ 🎧 〈思考力・判断力・表現力〉各話者の発話の要点を整理して比較・判断できる。　**Lesson 5** 21

□ 📖 〈思考力・判断力・表現力〉「集団生活についての英文」を読んで、概要を把握できる。

Reading　目標➡20分　　　　　　　　　　テーマ　生物　　15

速読問題 次の英文を2分で読んで、1. の問いに答えなさい。

　　In the early part of the twentieth century, an American naturalist came across (1)a strange sight in the *Guyana jungle.　A group of army ants was moving in (2)a huge circle.　The circle was 1,200 feet in *circumference, and it took each ant two and half hours to complete the *loop. The ants went around and around the circle for two days until most of them fell dead.

5　　What the naturalist saw was what biologists call (3)a "*circular mill."　The mill is created when army ants find themselves separated from their colony.　Once they're lost, they obey a simple rule: follow the ant in front of you.　The result is the mill, which usually only breaks up when a few ants stray from the circle by chance and the others follow them away.

　　An ant colony normally works remarkably well.　No one ant manages the colony.　No one
10　gives orders.　Each individual ant alone knows almost nothing.　Yet the colony successfully finds food, gets all its work done, and reproduces itself.　But their mutual dependence, which makes ants so successful, is also responsible for the unfortunate death of the ants in the circular mill.　Every move that an ant makes depends on what its fellow ants do, and an ant cannot act independently, (4)which would help break the march to death.

15　　Human beings are not ants.　In other words, human beings can make their decisions independently.　Independence doesn't mean isolation, but it does mean a certain freedom from the influence of others.　If we are independent, our opinions are, in some sense, our own.

　　Independence is important to intelligent decision making for two reasons.　First, it will prevent the mistakes that people make from influencing one another.　Second, independent
20　individuals are more likely to have new information rather than the same old data that everyone is already familiar with.　The best groups, then, are made up of people with different viewpoints who are able to stay independent of each other.　You can be a one-sided and irrational person, but as long as you're independent, you won't make the group any more blind than those ants do.

（356 words／東北学院大）

²Guyana[gaɪǽnə]：ガイアナ(南米の共和国)　　³circumference[sərkʌ́mf(ə)r(ə)ns]：円周、周囲
³loop[lúːp]：輪、環　　⁵circular mill：ぐるぐる回り

1. この英文は全体として何について述べていますか。一つ選びなさい。　　　　　　　　　　（4点）
   a. The importance of being in harmony with society.
   b. The importance of decisions made by each individual.
   c. The importance of following the majority.
   d. The importance of isolation from society.

精 読問題 もう一度英文を読んで、次の問いに答えなさい。

2. 下線部(1)の具体的な内容を、50字程度の日本語で説明しなさい。　　　　　　　　　　（7点）

（解答欄 50字）

3. 下線部(2)の大きさを、具体的に日本語で説明しなさい。　　　　　　　　　　　　　　（6点）

4. 下線部(3)について、　　　　　　　　　　　　　　　　　　　　　　　　　　　　　（各5点）
   ⑴ それが作られるのはアリのどのような習性が原因なのかがわかる部分を英語で抜き出しなさい。

   ⑵ 人間社会における何の例として挙げられているか。最終パラグラフから1語で抜き出しなさい。
   （　　　　　　　）

5. 下線部(4)の解釈として最も適当なものを一つ選びなさい。　　　　　　　　　　　　　（3点）
   a. every move that an ant makes would help break the march to death
   b. what its fellow ants do would help break the march to death
   c. an ant cannot act independently, so it would help break the march to death
   d. if an ant acted independently, it would help break the march to death

6. 全体把握 本文の内容と合っていないものをすべて選びなさい。　　　　　　　　　　　（5点）
   a. The circular mill is a new colony of the ants which have been separated from their colony.
   b. The mill may break up when a few ants stray from the circle.
   c. Ants have no leader or governor in their society; they are dependent on each other.
   d. Ants' mutual dependence helps them to survive, but it sometimes kills them.
   e. Human beings are quite different from ants in that we can make our own decision.
   f. Independence is one thing, and isolation is another.
   g. Our society should be made up of people dependent on the others' opinions and views.
   h. If the ants could act independently, they would be less likely to march to death.

Grammar & Usage　目標➡ 7分

1 次の各文の　□　に入れるのに最も適当なものを選びなさい。　（各2点）

1. Robin suddenly began to feel nervous □ the interview.
   a. during　　　b. by　　　c. while　　　d. until

2. Julia is now 18, so she's quite □ of looking after herself.　〈南山大〉
   a. capable　　　b. fitted　　　c. qualified　　　d. used

3. The office staff consisted mainly □ women.　〈立命館大〉
   a. for　　　b. from　　　c. in　　　d. of

4. He is, □ , an honest and reliable man.　〈関西学院大〉
   a. in the best of my knowledge　　　b. of my best knowledge
   c. to the best of my knowledge　　　d. the best I know

5. You must try to win, but □ all, you must play fairly.　〈上智大〉
   a. with　　　b. out of　　　c. above　　　d. at

6. □ the two government leaders have reached an agreement, there will be peace.
   a. For that　　　b. Now that　　　c. Since that　　　d. Upon that

2 次の会話の　□　に入れるのに最も適当なものを選びなさい。　（各3点）

1. A : Have you seen Yuko recently?
   B : No, but □ dinner with her on Sunday.
   a. I'm having　　　b. I've been having　　c. I'd have　　　d. I've had

2. A : Hurry up or we'll be late!
   B : Don't worry. I'll be ready □ two minutes.
   a. after　　　b. by　　　c. for　　　d. in

3. A : Dinner's □ me tonight. Order whatever you like.
   B : Thanks, I think I'll have spaghetti.　〈上智大〉
   a. with　　　b. on　　　c. for　　　d. to

Writing　目標➡ 3分

3 1は（　）内の語を並べかえなさい。2、3は英訳しなさい。　（1：3点／2、3：各6点）

1. 助けが必要なときは、遠慮なく言ってください。（1語不要）　〈青山学院大〉
   (any / care / not / ask / if / do / hesitate / you / need / help / to).

2. この手紙がロンドンに着くまで、どのくらい時間がかかりますか。　〈学習院大〉
   How _____ ＿＿＿＿＿＿＿＿＿＿＿＿＿＿＿＿ London?

3. 真夜中を過ぎてやっと宿題をやり終えた。　〈高知大〉
   ＿＿＿＿＿＿＿＿＿＿＿＿＿＿＿＿＿＿＿＿＿＿

CAN-DO List □ 〈知識・技能〉ランダムに配列された文法・語法に関する問題に答えることができる。

4 英文を聞き、空欄1～4に入れるのに最も適当なものを一つずつ選びなさい。 （各2点）

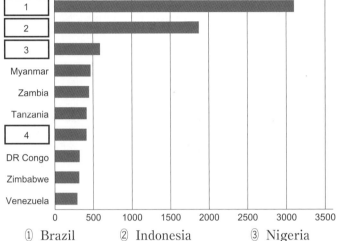

(1000ha)

| 1 |
| 2 |
| 3 |
| Myanmar |
| Zambia |
| Tanzania |
| 4 |
| DR Congo |
| Zimbabwe |
| Venezuela |

0　500　1000　1500　2000　2500　3000　3500

① Brazil　② Indonesia　③ Nigeria　④ Sudan

Rapid Reading 目標➡5分 　テーマ 地球温暖化 共通テスト

5 グラフを読み取って、問いに対する答えとして最も適当なものを一つずつ選びなさい。 （各6点）

The influence of greenhouse gases on global warming (2001)

Methane 20%
Chlorofluorocarbon 14%
Carbon dioxide 60%
2001
Others 6%

China 30.3%
2013
Others 29.3%
USA 15.3%
EU 10.1%
India 6.0%
Japan 3.7%
Russia 5.3%
Total 9.2 billion tons
Major carbon dioxide emitting countries (2013)

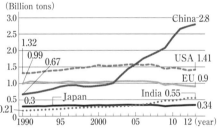

The amount of carbon dioxide emitted by the major countries

(Billion tons)
3.0 — China 2.8
2.5
2.0 — 1.32
1.5 — 0.99 / 0.67 — USA 1.41
1.0 — EU 0.9
0.5 — 0.3 — Japan — India 0.55
0.21 — 0.34
1990　95　2000　05　10 12 (year)

1. Which of the following statements is true?
   ① China's amount of emissions of carbon dioxide in 2012 was five times as much as in 1990.
   ② In 2013, Japan emitted more than a billion tons of carbon dioxide.
   ③ In 2013, the top three countries emitting carbon dioxide were China, USA and India.
   ④ We can ignore the emissions of methane and chlorofluorocarbon in preventing global warming.

2. Which of the following statements is best supported by the above graphs?
   ① Japan should purchase more carbon dioxide emission rights than other countries.
   ② Forest fires are the major cause of carbon dioxide emission.
   ③ The key to preventing global warming is the reduction of carbon dioxide emissions.
   ④ There is no relationship between global warming and economics.

Reading　目標➡20分　　　　　　テーマ　環境問題　　17

速読問題　次の英文を2.5分で読んで、1. の問いに答えなさい。

When global warming caused by increased greenhouse gases first became an issue, some people said it was just a natural cycle and that human activity was unrelated.　Scientists have long agreed that there are natural cycles of cooling and heating.　However, in recent years, due to improvements in scientific analysis, most scientists now believe (1)humans are
5　contributing greatly to the problem, too.

Greenhouse gases are various gases such as carbon dioxide (CO_2), methane (CH_4), ozone (O_3) and some others.　A lot of these gases are stored in the earth or sea, but a lot of them go into the atmosphere.　An increase of these gases traps more heat from the sun in our earth's atmosphere.　As a result, ocean temperatures are rising, causing ice at the poles to melt.
10　This will cause sea levels to rise.　Populated areas along the sea coasts will be covered in water. Cities will be covered with water. Food production will decrease, too.　The consequences will be hugely negative for human life on earth.

(2)What makes the picture more complex is the role of what are termed "aerosols."　Aerosols are small particles carried in the atmosphere.　Some come from burning fossil fuels (such as
15　coal and diesel) and are black.　These black aerosols help to heat the earth's atmosphere because they absorb heat from sunlight.　However, many of the aerosols produced by burning fossil fuels and other materials are light in color and are reflective.　That is, they reflect the sun's light and cause cooling.

The problem is that it has been very difficult to measure the amount of reflective aerosols in
20　the atmosphere, whereas measurements of CO_2 have become very accurate.　Thus, we don't really know at which point the amount of CO_2 in the atmosphere will reach the "tipping point," that is, the point when humans will no longer be able to solve the problem.　Some scientists used to say that the critical point was 450 parts per million (we are presently at about 390 ppm of CO_2 in the atmosphere).　Now, however, they say it could be much less than that.　(3)They
25　are just not very sure.

Thus, humans are faced with a decision.　Should we immediately cut down on our fossil fuel use even though doing so will cause great economic problems?　Or should we continue using fossil fuels at the present rate and hope that it balances out in the end?　Now is the time for a decision.

(408 words / 昭和女子大)

26　│　CAN-DO List　□　🔍　〈知識・技能〉「環境問題」をテーマとした英文の展開を的確に理解することができる。

	Grammar Usage	Writing	Listening	Rapid Reading	Reading	Total
	/21	/15	/8	/12	/44	/100

1. 筆者が最も言いたいことを、一つ選びなさい。 （5点）

  a. How does global warming come about?

  b. Now is the time when we have to decide whether we continue to use fossil fuels.

  c. There are some aerosols which may prevent global warming.

  d. Under global warming, what will become of the earth?

精 読問題 もう一度英文を読んで、次の問いに答えなさい。

2. 下線部(1)とほぼ同じ意味になるように、（　　）内に適語を補いなさい。 （5点）

  Humans are the major (　　　　　　　) of the problem.

3. 下線部(2)について、なぜエーロゾルが地球温暖化の全体像を複雑にしていると言えるのか。
下線部(2)と同じパラグラフの内容から、日本語で説明しなさい。 （6点）

_____

_____

4. 下線部(3)について、科学者は何に確信が持てないのか。またそれはどのような理由か。
それぞれ日本語で説明しなさい。 （各4点）

  確信が持てないもの：_____

  理由：_____

5. 全体把握 ☐ に入れるのに最も適当なものを、一つずつ選びなさい。 （各4点）

  (1) Recent scientific evidence shows that global warming is ☐ .

    a. caused only by humans　　　　　b. caused only by natural cycles

    c. caused both by natural cycles and humans

    d. not as big a problem as we thought earlier

  (2) The temperature of the oceans is rising because of an increase in ☐ .

    a. greenhouse gases that are stored in them

    b. greenhouse gases that are trapped in polar ice

    c. temperatures of the land　　　　d. greenhouse gases in the atmosphere

  (3) "Aerosols" are ☐ .

    a. pieces of dust in the air　　　　b. black gases in the air

    c. a kind of fossil fuel　　　　　　d. particles of sunlight

  (4) Scientists thought the "tipping point" of CO_2 in the atmosphere was ☐ .

    a. 450 parts per million　　　　　b. 390 parts per million

    c. 300 parts per million　　　　　d. less than 450 parts per million

  (5) According to the graph, CO_2 ☐ .

    a. increased from 275 ppm in 1750 to 325 ppm in 1900

    b. decreased from 1750 to 1800

    c. increased most rapidly from 1950 to 2000

    d. has increased slowly from 1750 until today

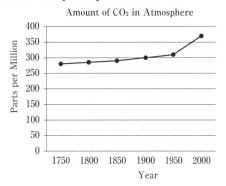

Amount of CO_2 in Atmosphere

Lesson 7

Grammar & Usage 目標➡7分

1 次の各文の ☐ に入れるのに最も適当なものを選びなさい。 （各2点）

1. Most young people would rather spend money than ☐ it in the bank.
   a. having put　　b. put　　　　　c. to put　　　　d. putting

2. There was an audience of ☐ four thousand at the concert yesterday.　〈関西学院大〉
   a. no less than　b. any less than　c. still more　　d. quite a few

3. He has ☐ information than his brother.　〈青山学院大〉
   a. fewer　　　　b. much　　　　c. less　　　　d. for

4. Max tried on six pairs of shoes, ☐ he liked.　〈日本女子大〉
   a. none of that　b. none of which　c. that none　　d. which none

5. ☐ busy I am in the morning, I make a point of glancing at the newspaper.〈南山大〉
   a. Although　　b. Even if　　　c. No matter how　d. Whatever

2 次の各組の文がほぼ同じ意味になるように、（　）内に適語を補いなさい。 （各4点）

1. They served better food at that restaurant before the new manager came.
   The quality of the food at that restaurant has declined ever (　　　　) the arrival of the new manager.　〈学習院大〉

2. The station clock showed half past eight.
   (　　　　)(　　　　) the station clock, it was half past eight.　〈福島大〉

3. The bird was half the size of an eagle.
   The bird was half (　　　　)(　　　　) as an eagle.　〈鹿児島大〉

4. Bud gave me his pen, so I gave him some marbles.
   Bud gave me his pen, and I gave him some marbles in (　　　　).　〈立教大〉

Writing 目標➡3分

3 1、2は（　）内の語句を並べかえなさい。3、4は英訳しなさい。 （1、2：各3点／3、4：各6点）

1. わずかなお金をためるのに、かなりの時間を浪費することもあるでしょう。　〈立命館大〉
   We could waste (time / to / lot / trying / a / save / of) a little money.

2. Ned shouted, "Watch out!" when he (a little child / into / saw / step out / the street) right in the path of a car.

3. この大学の入学試験を受けることにしたのはどうしてですか。　〈関西学院大〉
   What made ＿＿＿＿＿＿＿＿＿＿＿＿＿＿＿＿＿＿＿?

4. 歌は私たちの生活に密接に結びついている。　〈学習院大〉
   Songs ＿＿＿＿＿＿＿＿＿＿＿＿＿＿＿＿＿＿＿.

Listening

目標➡5分　　テーマ 仕事・休日　英検®　◀)) 18〜19

4 英文と質問を聞き、その答えとして最も適当なものを一つずつ選びなさい。 (各5点)

1. ① 3.
   ② 5.
   ③ 15.
   ④ 18.

2. ① Yumi can take a Yoga lesson every week.
   ② Yumi can take a Yoga lesson on the second and fourth Saturdays.
   ③ Yumi has to give up taking a Yoga lesson on Saturdays.
   ④ Yumi's boss is going to work on Saturdays once every two weeks.

Rapid Reading

目標➡5分　　テーマ ストレス　共通テスト

5 グラフを読み取って、問いに対する答えとして最も適当なものを一つずつ選びなさい。 (各5点)

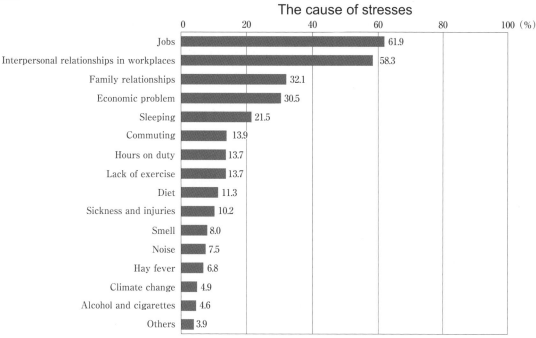

The cause of stresses

	(%)
Jobs	61.9
Interpersonal relationships in workplaces	58.3
Family relationships	32.1
Economic problem	30.5
Sleeping	21.5
Commuting	13.9
Hours on duty	13.7
Lack of exercise	13.7
Diet	11.3
Sickness and injuries	10.2
Smell	8.0
Noise	7.5
Hay fever	6.8
Climate change	4.9
Alcohol and cigarettes	4.6
Others	3.9

1. Which of the following statements is true?
   ① Alcohol and cigarettes aren't related to stress.
   ② Half or more of the people are under stress related to their jobs and interpersonal relationships in their workplaces.
   ③ People feel more stress about economic problems than any other cause of stress.
   ④ Noise is one of the main causes of stress.

2. Which of the following statements is best supported by the above graph?
   ① A counselor should be permanently stationed in companies.
   ② Japan's economy is now in good shape.
   ③ People should get rid of job-related stress by doing sports.
   ④ Young people are under stress related to child rearing.

CAN-DO List　□ 〈思考力・判断力・表現力〉「仕事・休日」に関する英語を聞き取り、理解できる。
　　　　　　　□ 〈思考力・判断力・表現力〉「ストレスのグラフ」を読んで情報を得ることができる。

Lesson 7 | 29

速読問題 次の英文を2.5分で読んで、1. の問いに答えなさい。

It is well known that stress affects workers' health.　When workers are not well, they tend to miss many days of work every year.　The organizations they work for are, in turn, not as productive as they should be.　However, levels of stress in different occupations, and the ways that workers relieve such stress, have not been studied in depth.　The Occupational
5　Psychology Association (OPA), therefore, conducted a survey on the effects of stress on workers in four different occupations and on the methods they use to relieve workplace stress.

The OPA researchers interviewed 100 workers in each of four occupations: nurses, air traffic controllers (ATCs), computer programmers, and junior high school teachers.　The workers were asked about the kinds of stress symptoms they had and how they dealt with
10　stressful situations.

The four types of stress symptoms mentioned most often were high blood pressure, overeating, depression, and sleeplessness.　The OPA researchers found that workers in the different occupations reported different frequencies of these stress symptoms.

The nurses reported that they ate more when they felt stressed.　The ATCs were more
15　affected by high blood pressure than other disorders.　Many of the computer programmers tended to feel nervous and anxious.　The teachers reported that they could not sleep well.

The researchers found that workers used five main methods to fight stress both at work and at home.　They were interested in how these ways of fighting stress differed in the four occupations.　The figure below shows how people in the four occupations relieved stress.

20　Stress Relief Methods

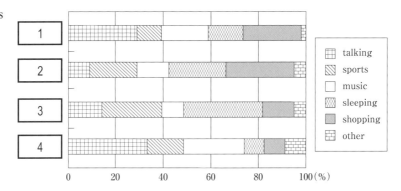

The nurses interviewed claimed that talking to others and shopping were the usual ways to relieve stress.　They also said that they liked listening to music from time to time.　The ATCs claimed that the responsibility for hundreds of lives on the job put a lot of pressure on them.　They relieved ₍₁₎this stress by shopping or sleeping, and when possible by playing sports.　The computer programmers, on the other hand, preferred sleeping and playing sports as the best ways to escape the effects of any stress.　They said that shopping, talking to others, and listening to music were less frequently used methods of stress relief for them.　The teachers preferred talking with other teachers as well as listening to music, particularly classical music, as the best ways to relieve stress.

　The OPA researchers concluded that workers in different jobs have different types of stress symptoms and employ different ways of relieving stress.　　　　　　　(407 words)

1．この英文は全体として何について述べているか。一つ選びなさい。　　　　　　（5点）
　　a．The influence stress may have on workers.
　　b．The results of stress and how to overcome it in various jobs.
　　c．The size of stress in various jobs.
　　d．The way people can get rid of stress inside their houses.

精 読問題 もう一度英文を読んで、次の問いに答えなさい。

2．グラフ中の空欄1～4に入れるのに最も適当なものを一つずつ選びなさい。　　（7点）
　　a．ATC　　　　　　　　b．Nurse　　　　　　　c．Programmer　　　　d．Teacher
　　1．(　　　)　　　　　　2．(　　　)　　　　　　3．(　　　)　　　　　4．(　　　)

3．下線部⑴について、航空管制官が抱えるストレスはどのようなことに起因しているか。英語で抜き出しなさい。　　　　　　　　　　　　　　　　　　　　　　　　　　　　　　　（8点）

4．**全体把握** ▭ に入れるのに最も適当なものを、一つずつ選びなさい。　　（各4点）
　　⑴ The main reason for conducting the OPA survey was to study ▭ .
　　　　a．the relation between occupations and stress
　　　　b．ways to reduce the number of workdays missed
　　　　c．the most stressful jobs　　　　　　d．ways to increase productivity
　　⑵ The stress symptom many of the programmers had was ▭ .
　　　　a．high blood pressure　　　　　　　　b．overeating
　　　　c．sleeplessness　　　　　　　　　　　d．depression
　　⑶ Among the workers in the four occupations, ▭ in particular said they suffered from severe stress while working.
　　　　a．programmers　　b．nurses　　　　c．teachers　　　　　d．ATCs
　　⑷ The survey found that, among the people interviewed, ▭ .
　　　　a．more programmers than ATCs reported that music relieved stress
　　　　b．classical music was highly effective for most groups in relieving stress
　　　　c．ATCs and nurses chose shopping more often than sports to relieve stress
　　　　d．both teachers and nurses favored shopping as a means of getting rid of stress

Lesson 8

Grammar & Usage　目標➡ 7分

1 次の各文の下線部とほぼ同じ意味を表すものを選びなさい。　　　　　　　（各3点）

1. Helen was able to <u>make sense of</u> this article completely.　〈日本大〉
   a. check　　　　b. review　　　　c. summarize　　　d. understand

2. John <u>came up with</u> a fascinating suggestion.　〈関西外国語大〉
   a. thought of　　b. denied　　　　c. turned down　　d. overtook

3. I <u>was getting along</u> with her until she insulted me.　〈立命館大〉
   a. traveled　　　b. competed　　　c. was angry　　　d. was friendly

4. John was <u>rejected</u> for the post because of his bad behavior.　〈関西外国語大〉
   a. brought out　b. turned down　c. accepted　　　d. called down

5. She will be here to <u>show off</u> her new dress.　〈駒澤大〉
   a. distribute　　b. disappoint　　c. display　　　　d. dissatisfy

6. She will <u>get in touch with</u> you by letter.　〈駒澤大〉
   a. content　　　b. contact　　　　c. contest　　　　d. contract

7. *A :* Do you need the copier?
   B : <u>After you</u>.　〈関西外国語大〉
   a. Go ahead　　b. I'll go with you　c. Take it　　　d. Before me

8. I don't like John; he is always <u>pulling my leg</u>.　〈立命館大〉
   a. teasing me　　　　　　　　　b. disturbing me
   c. speaking ill of me　　　　　　d. looking down on me

Writing　目標➡ 3分

2 1、2は（　　）内の語句を並べかえなさい。3、4は英訳しなさい。　（1、2：各3点／3、4：各6点）

1. It is impossible to (a / all / carry on / conversation / with) this noise in the background.
   〈立教大〉

   _____

2. Being the eldest son, my father thinks (mother / is / his / responsible / taking / care / for / he / of).
   〈静岡県立大〉

   _____

3. 私はアメリカの大学で一年、英文学を勉強した。　〈島根大〉

   _____

4. 今日では多くの外国人が、日本語をコミュニケーションの手段として使っている。〈日本女子大〉

   _____

Listening

目標➡5分　　テーマ 進路　共通テスト　🔊 21

3 話を聞き、示された条件に最も合うものを一つ選びなさい。　　　　　　　　（10点）

> 状況
>
> あなたは将来、薬剤師を目指して大学を選びたいと思い、4つの大学の広報担当の話を聞いています。
>
> あなたが考えている条件
>
> A. 最新の設備が整っていること。
> B. 少人数制であること。
> C. 患者のケアの方法について教えてくれること。

[　　] is the university you are most likely to choose.

① The University of Apple College of Pharmacy　　② The University of Beans

③ The University of Cinnamon　　④ The Durian University

Rapid Reading

目標➡5分　　　　　　　　　　　　　　　テーマ 労働

4 次の英文は、日本のコンビニで働くことを考えている香港からの留学生の記事です。
内容を読み、問いに対する答えとして最も適当なものを一つずつ選びなさい。　（各5点）

> There are more than 58,000 convenience stores in Japan.　The owners are employing more and more foreign staff members.　I interviewed two part-time workers from Hong Kong and China, and asked them about positive and negative aspects at work.
>
> Nicholas, from Hong Kong, said, "It was good to have more opportunities to speak Japanese.　Through the experience, I met various customers and staff members.　It was true there were some difficult customers, but most were friendly."
>
> On the other hand, Zhang Xinyu, from China, said, "There were some customers I couldn't make friends with.　One said to me 'The usual' when ordering and I had no idea what they wanted.　Some even told me to 'go back to China,' when they noticed my name written in *katakana*.　I was very sad because I was discriminated against when I was just doing my duty."
>
> Working at a convenience store will give me good and bad experiences.　However, this will help me learn Japanese culture in depth.

1. What is suggested about working at a convenience store in Japan?

   ① It will be a good occasion to learn Japanese as a foreign language.

   ② Nicholas said that he had few opportunities to speak Japanese.

   ③ The work will help Chinese culture spread among the people in the community.

   ④ There are over 58,000 convenience stores where foreign staff members work.

2. Why was it difficult for Zhang Xinyu to work at a convenience store in Japan?

   ① Her customers did not understand the phrase, "The usual."

   ② She could not do what she should do as a store clerk.

   ③ She felt sad because she couldn't remember what to do as a store clerk.

   ④ Some customers took a negative attitude toward her.

 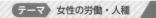
テーマ 女性の労働・人種

速読問題 次の英文は、アメリカ合衆国の航空技術開発で重要な役割を果たした黒人女性「計算手」("computers")たちについて述べたものです。英文を2.5分で読んで、1.の問いに答えなさい。

As America moved towards the Second World War, the push for aeronautical advancement grew ever greater, creating a strong demand for mathematicians. Women were the solution. They were hired by the Langley Memorial Aeronautical Laboratory in 1935 to shoulder the burden of calculating. (1)Women acted as human "computers," freeing the engineers of hand
5 calculations in the decades before the digital age. Sharp and successful, the female population at Langley rapidly increased.

Many of these computers are finally getting recognition. However, (2)the efforts contributed by courageous African-American women are clearly missing from the history of female achievement. These black computers helped open a path for mathematicians and
10 engineers of all races and genders to follow.

Built in 1917, Langley was the headquarters for (3)the National Advisory Committee for Aeronautics (NACA), which was intended to turn the aircraft of the day into war machines. In 1958 this organization was replaced by the National Aeronautics and Space Administration (NASA) as the space race gained speed.

15 Langley was not just a laboratory of science and engineering; in many ways, it was also a racial laboratory, a gender relations laboratory. The researchers came from across America. Many came from parts of the country (4)sympathetic to the early Civil Rights Movement, and (5)backed the progressive ideals of expanded freedoms for black citizens and women.

But life at Langley wasn't without any problems. Not only were the women rarely
20 provided the same opportunities and titles as their male counterparts, but the black computers lived with the reality that they were (6)second-class citizens.

For example, there was an incident when a racist sign ordering the black women to sit separately from the other workers was placed in the dining room. One particularly brave computer, Miriam Mann, removed the racist sign from the table. When the sign returned,
25 she removed it again. That showed incredible courage. This was still a time when African-American people could be ordered to get off the bus for sitting in the white seating area. But eventually Mann won. The sign disappeared. The women fought many more of these seemingly small battles, against separate bathrooms and restricted access to meetings.

History is the sum total of what people do on a daily basis. People think of history as being
30 these (7)huge figures —— George Washington and Martin Luther King. Even so, people go to

CAN-DO List ☐ 〈思考力・判断力・表現力〉「人種・ジェンダー」をテーマとした英文の展開を的確に理解することができる。

bed at night, wake up the next morning, and then yesterday is (8)history.   These small actions in some ways are as important as the individual actions by these famous figures.

(418 words / 日本女子大)

1．この英文のタイトルとして最も適当なものを一つ選びなさい。 （5点）

   a．A True Story of "Hidden Figures"

   b．History Made by "Huge Figures"

   c．Small Actions Change the World

   d．The Development of Computers by Black Women

精 読問題 もう一度英文を読んで、次の問いに答えなさい。

2．下線部(1)について、具体的にはどのようなことか。日本語で説明しなさい。 （5点）

_____

3．下線部(2)の the efforts はどのようなことに役立ったのか。日本語で説明しなさい。 （5点）

_____

4．下線部(3)の NACA が NASA に取って代わられた理由は何か。一つ選びなさい。 （4点）

   a．宇宙開発競争が一般化したから   b．宇宙開発競争が加速したから

   c．宇宙開発の勢いが衰えたから   d．宇宙空間で競争が始まったから

5．下線部(4)～(7)の意味として最も適当なものを一つずつ選びなさい。 （各1点）

  (4) a．共感して   b．参加して   c．支援して   d．反対して

  (5) a．後退した   b．支持した   c．証明した   d．反対した

  (6) a．十分な権利を保障されなかった市民   b．二等列車しか使えない市民

      c．2つの階級を持っている市民   d．古着を着用していた市民

  (7) a．偉大な功績   b．大柄な人物   c．莫大な数字   d．有名な人物

6．下線部(8)の history が重要視する二つの要素はどのようなものか。日本語で説明しなさい。

（各5点）

  ・_____

  ・_____

7． 全体把握 本文の内容と合っているものをすべて選びなさい。 （5点）

   a．The computers at Langley were mainly used by female mathematicians.

   b．African-American women were hired at Langley to do calculations by hand.

   c．Langley did not hire any women until the 1950s.

   d．Miriam Mann was one of the first female astronauts.

   e．There was a lack of racial equality among the Langley workers.

   f．History focuses more on people's small actions than the individual actions of famous people.

Grammar & Usage　目標➡ 7分

1 次の各文の ☐ に入れるのに最も適当なものを選びなさい。　　　　　　（各2点）

1. My mother is making a fast ☐ after the operation on her knee last week.
   a. repair　　　　　b. treatment　　　　c. recovery　　　　d. benefit

2. I want to buy some drink but only have a five-dollar bill.　I need some ☐ .
   a. change　　　　　b. small cash　　　　c. little money　　　d. return

3. A ☐ is the money that you pay for a journey made, for example, by bus, train, or taxi.
   a. charge　　　　　b. cost　　　　　　　c. fare　　　　　　d. fee

4. I want to be ☐ with everyone in the class.　　　　　　　　　〈上智大〉
   a. the friend　　　　b. friends　　　　　c. friend　　　　　d. the friends

5. My sister can't ☐ any secret to herself even for an hour.　　　〈上智大〉
   a. keep　　　　　　b. make　　　　　　c. take　　　　　　d. protect

6. The Olympic Games are held ☐ four years.　　　　　　　　　〈上智大〉
   a. all　　　　　　　b. each　　　　　　c. every　　　　　d. for

2 次の各文の下線部のうちから誤りを含むものを一つずつ選びなさい。　　（各3点）

1. a.The trouble is we are so busy b.to prepare for the class c.that we do not have d.enough time for club activities.　　　　　　　　　　　　　　　　〈青山学院大〉

2. a.Although Bob prefers b.walking c.than taking the bus, he often uses the public transportation d.to save time.　　　　　　　　　　　　　　　　　〈法政大〉

3. a.Almost students were b.present at the meeting, c.though many teachers were d.absent.

4. One of the a.reason why women live longer than men b.is their ability to make close friends c.with d.whom they share their sorrows.　　　　　　　　〈上智大〉

Writing　目標➡ 3分

3 1、2は（　　）内の語句を並べかえなさい。3は英訳しなさい。　（1、2：各3点／3：6点）

1. 健康は、失って初めてそのありがたみがわかる。　　　　　　　　〈実践女子大〉

   We (blessing / don't / health / it / know / lose / of / the / until / we).

   _____

2. Traveling abroad is exciting for many people.　There are, however, a few who miss their own (become / countries / so much / that / they) homesick.

   _____

3. 彼女が試験に合格しようがしまいが、大した問題ではない。　　　　〈聖心女子大〉

   _____

Listening

目標➡5分 　　テーマ 水 GTEC®　🔊 23〜24

4 英語の質問と、それに対する応答が4つ読まれます。応答として最も適当なものを一つずつ選び
なさい。 　　　　　　　　　　　　　　　　　　　　　　　　　　　　　　　　（各5点）

1. ① ② ③ ④ 　　　　　　　　　　2. ① ② ③ ④

Rapid Reading

目標➡5分 　　テーマ 水問題 英検®

5 （1）・（2）に入れるのに最も適当なものを一つずつ選びなさい。 　　　　（各5点）

Houses in Tonle Sap

　　Have you ever heard about Tonle Sap Lake in Cambodia? 　It is the largest freshwater lake
in Southeast Asia. 　Over one million people live around the lake or in floating houses on it.
Until recent years, however, （　1　） for sanitation were not available to the floating houses,
so the lake had been getting polluted by sewage for a long time. 　People there had to get all the
water they needed for their lives from the river. 　However, from 2015, WATERAID, an NGO,
started to supply the Handypod to the people living on Tonle Sap. 　This device filters toilet
waste before it flows into the lake and helps keep the water clean. 　（　2　）, more people on
Tonle Sap now have better access to cleaner water.

1.
　① enough water to stay healthy 　　② good equipment and systems
　③ good plants and facilities 　　　　④ nice air-conditioners and ventilators

2.
　① As a result 　　　　　　　　　　② In addition
　③ In contrast 　　　　　　　　　　④ On the other hand

Reading 目標➡20分 テーマ 水問題 25

速読問題 次の英文を2.5分で読んで、1. の問いに答えなさい。

An estimated 70 percent of the water consumed worldwide is used by farmers, while some 20 percent is used by industry and 10 percent for residential purposes.   In the increasingly intense competition for water among these three sectors, the economics of water do not favor agriculture.   In China, 1,000 tons of water can be used to produce one ton of wheat, worth
5　perhaps $200, or else to increase industrial output by $14,000——70 times as much.   In a country that is desperately seeking economic growth and the jobs it generates, (1)shifting water from agriculture to industry is an obvious strategy.

　　(2)Urbanization and industrialization also expand the demand for water.   As developing country villagers, traditionally dependent on the village well, move to urban high-rise
10　apartment buildings, their domestic water use can easily triple.   Industrial development takes even more water than the population shift from rural to urban areas.   Rising affluence in itself generates additional demands for water.   For example, as people move up the social and economic ladder, consuming more beef, pork, chicken, eggs, and other stock farm products, they use more grain.   (3)A diet rich in those products, such as in the United States,
15　requires four times as much grain per person as a rice-based diet in a country like India. Using four times as much grain means using four times as much water.

　　Once a local phenomenon, water shortages are now crossing national borders via the international grain trade.   The world's fastest-growing grain import market is North Africa and the Middle East.   Virtually every country in these regions is also experiencing water
20　shortages and rapid population growth.   As the demand for water in the regions' cities and industries rises, it is typically satisfied by shifting water from its traditional use in the fields. The loss in food production capacity is then compensated for by importing grain from abroad. Since one ton of grain represents 1,000 tons of water, (4)this is the most efficient way for water-poor countries.

25　The water required to produce the grain and other food products imported into North Africa and the Middle East is roughly equal to the annual flow of the Nile River.   Stated otherwise, the fast-growing water shortages of these regions are equal to another Nile flowing into the regions in the form of imported grain.   It is often said that future wars in the regions will more likely be fought over water than oil.   Perhaps, but given the difficulty in winning a
30　water war, the competition for water seems more likely to take place in world grain markets.

　　The world water shortages grow larger each year, (5)making it progressively more difficult to manage.   If countries everywhere decided to halt the overpumping of groundwater, the world grain harvest would fall by some 160 million tons, and grain prices would *go off the top of the chart.   The longer countries delay in facing this issue, the wider the water shortages
35　become and the greater the eventual adjustment will be.   Unless governments in water-poor countries act quickly to make the population stable and to raise water productivity, their water shortages may soon become food shortages.

(519 words / 関西学院大)

³³ go off the top of the chart：大きすぎて測れなくなる

1．この英文の要約として最も適当な文を一つ選びなさい。 （5点）

   a．About 70% of the water shortages in the world are caused by urbanization and industrialization in developing countries.

   b．Countries everywhere decided to stop urbanization and industrialization because of the water shortages.

   c．Experiencing water shortages and rapid population growth cannot be stopped unless governments improve their policies for grain production.

   d．Water shortages caused by urbanization and industrialization will probably be the cause of food shortages in the future.

精 読問題 もう一度英文を読んで、次の問いに答えなさい。

2．下線部(1)の文中で表す内容に最も近いものを一つ選びなさい。 （3点）

   a．the benefits of using more water for agriculture than industry

   b．the gain in the number of jobs using a large amount of water

   c．the increase in the amount of water used for industry instead of agriculture

   d．the profit made from preventing water use by industry

3．下線部(2)の理由として考えられるものを次のうちから一つ選びなさい。 （3点）

   a．Becoming richer itself leads to the increasing demand for water.

   b．Industrial development makes rural people give up their farms.

   c．People in the country move to a rural area.

   d．Population shifts from rural to urban areas make the population larger.

4．下線部(3)は結果的に何を意味するのか。日本語で説明しなさい。 （8点）

5．下線部(4)の this が指す内容を日本語で答えなさい。 （8点）

6．下線部(5)を具体的に言いかえた文を、下線部(5)と同じパラグラフから抜き出しなさい。 （8点）

7．**全体把握** 本文の内容と合っているものをすべて選びなさい。 （9点）

   a．In China, people can gain an economic advantage by using water for agriculture rather than for industry.

   b．People who used to live in a village know how to secure a water supply even in a city.

   c．More water is needed because grain is used for animal feed as well as for human consumption.

   d．In North Africa and the Middle East, grains need to be imported because of the shift of water from agriculture to industry.

   e．The Nile River can cover the water shortage in the regions where people need to grow grains.

   f．Governments facing water shortages need to improve economic productivity before trying to manage population growth.

Lesson 10

Grammar & Usage 目標➡5分

1 次の各文の ▢ に入れるのに最も適当なものを選びなさい。　　　　　　　（各3点）

1. They seldom, if ▢ , go to their hometown in England.　　〈実践女子大〉
   - a. often
   - b. ever
   - c. never
   - d. rarely

2. ▢ you need any help, just let me know.　　〈学習院大〉
   - a. Could
   - b. Had
   - c. Should
   - d. Would

3. A few minutes' walk ▢ me to the ruins of Olympia.　　〈南山大〉
   - a. arrived
   - b. brought
   - c. came
   - d. reached

4. Since these glasses can break easily, you must handle them with ▢ .
   - a. trouble
   - b. danger
   - c. care
   - d. ease

5. Brian decided to take up jogging because he felt out of ▢ .　　〈青山学院大〉
   - a. mind
   - b. order
   - c. shape
   - d. sight

6. Bill had to leave his family ▢ when he went abroad to work.
   - a. back
   - b. behind
   - c. off
   - d. over

7. A : The idea that knowledge is only something to be learned at school is nonsense, don't you think?

   B : Yes, especially in a world as complicated and rapidly changing as ▢ .
   - a. its
   - b. ours
   - c. them
   - d. these

Writing 目標➡5分

2 1、2は（　　）内の語句を並べかえなさい。3、4は英訳しなさい。　（1、2：各3点／3、4：各6点）

1. Hospitals have to be very careful to match the blood type of the donor to (getting / of / the blood / the blood type / the person).

   _____

2. You said you would introduce me to (a car / a friend of yours / had / to / who) sell.

   _____

3. かつては大西洋を船で横断するのに何か月もかかったが、今では飛行機で2、3時間で横断できる。

   _____ in a ship, but now a plane can cross the Atlantic in a few hours.

4. 私は結婚する決心をしました。そして、世界のほかのだれよりもあなたと結婚したいと思っています。

   I've made up my mind to get married and _____.

CAN-DO List ▢ 〈知識・技能〉ランダムに配列された文法・語法に関する問題に答えることができる。

Listening 目標➡5分

3 英文を聞き、問いの答えとして最も適当なものを一つずつ選びなさい。 (各5点)

1. According to the lecture, which statement is true?
   ① In 2002, Assistance Dogs started to be raised and trained throughout Japan.
   ② People with an Assistance Dog must be accepted in any restaurant now.
   ③ Since 2002, the cost of supporting Assistance Dogs from birth to retirement has been increasing.
   ④ Since 2002, the number of Assistance Dogs has been increasing.

2. How are the organizations making money?
   ① Being supported by government funds.
   ② Charging fees for the use of dogs.
   ③ Mostly receiving donations from people.
   ④ Supplied from the savings of 6 million yen.

Rapid Reading 目標➡5分

4 (1)・(2)に入れるのに最も適当なものを一つずつ選びなさい。 (各5点)

For decades, specially trained guide dogs have been helping blind people "see." Now, dogs are also being trained to help deaf people "hear." Dogs in general have highly developed sense of hearing. A dog can hear a noise from a distance of 229 meters that most people (1). Hearing ear dogs are trained to *alert their *hearing-impaired owners to everyday sounds they cannot notice on their own. The simple act of being alerted to a knock at the door, an approach from behind, or the sound of an alarm signal allows the hearing-impaired to experience (2) that they could not have imagined.

⁴alert A to B：A(人)にBを気付かせる　　⁴hearing-impaired：聴覚障害のある

1. ① can hear beyond 23 meters
   ② can hear within 23 meters
   ③ can't hear beyond 23 meters
   ④ can't hear within 23 meters
2. ① a good sense of humor
   ② a sense of belonging
   ③ a sense of responsibility
   ④ a sense of self-confidence

Reading 目標➡20分 テーマ 社会福祉 27

速読問題 次の英文を2.5分で読んで、1. の問いに答えなさい。

The concept that trained dogs could act as eyes for those who could not see developed at the beginning of the twentieth century in Germany in an unusual school.   The pupils were not humans, but dogs who were taught how to lead people who were blind.   The idea caught on quickly, and guide dogs, or Seeing Eye dogs, began to be trained in many countries.   (1)These

5 patient and loyal animals lead their blind companions everywhere they go, permitting them to make their way in the world almost as well as sighted persons.

(2)Not every kind of dog makes a good guide.   Seeing Eye dogs must be alert at all times, so dogs that are easily distracted are not suitable.   The best kinds of guide dogs are smart, easy to train, and usually get along well with people.   During its training, the dog is taken to many

10 kinds of busy places.   This is to get it accustomed to anything that might happen.   A dog is trained in large stores, noisy airports, and crowded restaurants.   It rides on buses and in taxis. It is pushed and hit, and it learns to ignore anything that might cause its attention to wander.

The Seeing Eye dog is responsible for guiding its owner carefully past any objects in the way.   On busy sidewalks, the dog must skillfully walk around other people to make sure its

15 owner doesn't get pushed.   A guide dog is trained to come to a stop just before it reaches some stairs; this is the way it tells its owner to step up or down.   But even though it learns to follow orders, (3)a guide dog is also taught that sometimes it must disobey.   For example, if its owner tells it to cross a street when a car is coming, it won't respond until it is safe to cross. While it is being trained, a guide dog is never punished for making a mistake; instead it is

20 encouraged to do better by being rewarded when it behaves correctly.

When the training is complete, a guide dog is assigned to its new owner.   The two of them need to be compatible because they will be together for a long time.   The size, weight, and nature of both are taken into account.   From the beginning, a strong bond needs to develop between the dog and the owner.   Usually a guide dog stays with its owner for about ten years

25 before it retires.   Then, it often may go to live with friends of the owner and stay with them as an ordinary family pet for the rest of its life.

(435 words / 名古屋外国語大)

CAN-DO List □ 〈思考力・判断力・表現力〉「社会福祉」をテーマとした英文の展開を的確に理解することができる。

1. この英文は全体として何について述べているか。一つ選びなさい。　　　　　　（6点）

　　a．The abilities required for guide dogs.　　　b．The history of guide dogs.

　　c．The lifetime of guide dogs.　　　d．Training guide dogs.

精 読問題 もう一度英文を読んで、次の問いに答えなさい。

2. 下線部(1)の具体的な内容を、英語3語で抜き出しなさい。　　　　　　（5点）

　　(　　　　　　　) (　　　　　　　) (　　　　　　　)

3. 下線部(2)について、よい盲導犬になるのはどのような犬か。日本語で説明しなさい。　　　　　　（5点）

_____

4. 下線部(3)の理由を日本語で説明しなさい。　　　　　　（5点）

_____

5. 全体把握 次の問いに対する答えとして最も適当なものを、一つずつ選びなさい。　　　　　　（各4点）

　(1) What kind of dog makes the best guide dog?

　　a．A dog which is clever and sociable.

　　b．A dog which can push through crowded restaurants.

　　c．A dog which can drive a bus or a taxi.

　　d．A dog which lets its attention wander.

　(2) Which of these characteristics is NOT necessary for a guide dog?

　　a．It has to be able to keep its owner from dangerous situations.

　　b．It needs to get on well with its owner.

　　c．It has to understand how to cross a road safely.

　　d．It has to be obedient at all times.

　(3) What is important when a dog is chosen for an owner?

　　a．The dog must be as strong as its owner.

　　b．The dog and the owner must like each other.

　　c．The dog must be about the same size and weight as its owner.

　　d．The dog must be a neighbor's family pet.

　(4) What should we NOT do to a guide dog while it is being trained?

　　a．We should not take the dog to noisy airports or stores.

　　b．We should not punish the dog for doing something wrong.

　　c．We should not give a reward for good behavior.

　　d．We should not encourage the dog to do better.

　(5) What happened in Germany in the early 1900s?

　　a．A school to train Seeing Eye dogs was established.

　　b．Guide dogs were taught to teach blind people.

　　c．Guide dogs were trained to work in many countries.

　　d．Blind people and dogs studied together in an unusual school.

Grammar & Usage 目標➡ 7分

1 次の各文の（A）と（B）に入れるのに最も適当な組み合わせを選びなさい。 （各4点）

1. If I (A) you were here before I left home, I (B) your book with me.
   a. A : didn't know　　B : have brought　　b. A : had known　B : would have brought
   c. A : hadn't known　B : would bring　　d. A : knew　　　B : had brought

2. Angelina (A) me whether I (B) enjoyed the festival last Saturday.
   a. A : asked　　　　B : had　　　　b. A : asked　　　　B : have
   c. A : said to　　　B : had　　　　d. A : said to　　　B : have

3. I didn't immediately recognize Professor Smith at the conference yesterday. He
   (A) a suit and tie although he usually (B).
   a. A : didn't put on　　　B : does　　b. A : didn't put on　　　B : was
   c. A : wasn't wearing　B : does　　d. A : wasn't wearing　　B : was

4. (A) you've completed this required class, you (B) be able to graduate.
   a. A : If　　　　B : won't　　　b. A : Unless　　B : could
   c. A : Until　　　B : won't　　　d. A : While　　　B : would

5. The government recognizes that the number of children (A) falling on one hand,
   while life expectancy is increasing (B).
   a. A : are　　　B : on another　　b. A : are　　　B : on the other
   c. A : is　　　B : on another　　d. A : is　　　B : on the other

6. Not only (A) Margaret plan the trip to New York, but she (B) did all the packing
   for her family.
   a. A : could　　B : too　　　b. A : did　　　B : also
   c. A : does　　B : also　　　d. A : would　　B : too

Writing 目標➡ 3分

2 1、2は（　　）内の語句を並べかえなさい。3、4は英訳しなさい。 （1、2：各3点／3、4：各6点）

1. 彼はあなたの興味のありそうな本をたくさん持っている。
   He (interest / books / has / lot / you / might / of / that / a).　　　　〈愛媛大〉

   _____

2. In recent years, people have become more health-conscious and consequently (fat /
   have / reduced / the amount of / they) eat.

   _____

3. 大切なのはどう人生を生きるかであって、どれくらい長く生きるかではないのです。〈千葉大〉

   _____

4. イギリス人はどんなに小さい庭であれ庭付きの家に住むことを望みます。　　　〈中央大〉

CAN-DO List ☐ 🔖 〈思考力・判断力・表現力〉ランダムに配列された文法・語法に関する問題に答えることができる。

Listening 目標➡5分 テーマ 都会生活 🔊 28

3 会話を聞き、問いの答えとして最も適当なものを一つずつ選びなさい。 (各5点)

1. Why does Daniel think there are some bad points in moving to urban areas?
   ① Life in urban areas is not so convenient that people can easily get tired of it.
   ② Life in urban areas is too busy and people can become tired of it.
   ③ More and more people use a lot of energy to go to urban areas.
   ④ More people should enjoy convenient lives in rural areas.

2. Which is correct about Daniel's camping?
   ① Hc didn't enjoy it because there were too many other campers.
   ② He enjoyed it with his friends very much.
   ③ He felt sad because he was alone in the vast camping site.
   ④ He really enjoyed being alone in the quiet camping site.

Rapid Reading 目標➡5分 テーマ 人口

4 記事を読み取って、問いに対する答えとして最も適当なものを一つずつ選びなさい。 (各5点)

> The world's urban population has increased by twenty times since 1900, in spite of just a four-times increase in total world population. Currently the world's urban population is expanding at 1.78 percent per year, while rural population growth is about to stop and decline. If current trends continue, the number of people in cities in 2025 will have doubled from the total in 1990. This number is almost two-thirds of the world's population. Developing countries are expected to contribute about 90 percent of this increase. Rapid urbanization is occurring in Asia and Africa. Most of this population increase is occurring in cities of less than half a million (53 percent of the world urban population) and cities between 1 and 5 million (22 percent).

1. How much has the world population increased since 1900?
   ① It has decreased by 90 percent.   ② It has doubled.
   ③ It has increased four times over.   ④ It has increased by twenty times.

2. According to the article, which city is the most likely to experience rapid urbanization?

① Accra	② Kinshasa	③ Liverpool	④ Spokane
Ghana:	DR Congo:	England:	USA:
4,700,000 people	11,598,000 people	460,000 people	220,000 people

Reading

目標➡20分　　　　　　　　　　　　　テーマ 人口　 29

速読問題 次の英文を2.5分で読んで、1. の問いに答えなさい。

　In 2008, (1)our species *crossed a significant Rubicon of habitat: for the first time, a majority of us lived in cities.　We could now be called, as at least one anthropologist has suggested, Metro sapiens.　And we're not done.　Globally, 2 billion more people will move to cities in the next thirty years.　By 2030, there will be 590 million urbanites just in India.　China is already
5　half urban; so is Liberia, and the percentage of urbanites in Bangladesh and Kenya *quadrupled in recent years.

　(2)This momentous urban migration could be a good thing.　Cities are often the most creative, wealthiest and most energy-efficient places to live.　City dwellers typically experience better sanitation, nutrition, gender equality and access to health care than their
10　rural counterparts.　The world's growing megacities, though, are not generally the centers of enlightenment that we might hope.　In Kinshasa, a city of more than 11 million in the Democratic Republic of the Congo, per capita yearly income is $250.　Harvard economist Ed Glaeser has asked how a megacity with such a poor population can "be anything but a hell on earth?"　Making cities like Kinshasa livable, he argues, is "the great challenge of our
15　century."

　Cities will have to figure out how to cram more people into smaller areas without everyone going literally crazy.　Back in 1965, animal behaviorist Paul Leyhausen described what happened to cats in unnaturally crowded environments: they become more aggressive and *despotic, turning into a "*spiteful mob."　In similar conditions, (3)Norway rats forget how to
20　build nests and start eating their own.　In confined *primates, hormonal systems go wrong and reproduction can drop.　So what about us?　Extensive reviews of the medical literature show a 21 percent increase in anxiety disorders, a 39 percent increase in mood disorders and a doubled risk of *schizophrenia in city dwellers.　Urban living is associated with increased activity in (4)the brain's amygdala —— the fear center —— and in the perigenual anterior
25　cingulate cortex, a key region for regulating fear and stress.

　Now that I'd learned about the ways in which being in nature changes our brains for the better, it was time to figure out how to bring the lessons back to where most of us live, in cities.　(5)Here are some of the essential take-home ideas: we all need nearby nature; we benefit mentally and psychologically from having trees, bodies of water, and green spaces just
30　to look at; we should be smarter about landscaping our schools, hospitals, workplaces and neighborhoods so everyone gains.　We need quick visits to natural areas that engage our senses.　Everyone needs access to clean, quiet and safe natural refuges in a city.　Short exposures to nature can make us less aggressive, more creative, more civic-minded and healthier overall.

(460 words / 新潟大)

> [1] cross a Rubicon：決定的な一歩を踏み出す　　　[5] quadruple[kwɑ(:)drú:p(ə)l]：4倍になる
> [19] despotic[dɪspá(:)tɪk]：独裁的な　　　[19] spiteful[spáɪtf(ə)l]：悪意に満ちた
> [20] primate[práɪmət]：霊長類の動物　　　[23] schizophrenia[skìtsəfríːniə]：統合失調症

1．この英文のタイトルとして最も適当なものを一つ選びなさい。　　　　　　　　　　　（5点）

   a．How Should Urban Lifestyles be Improved?

   b．What Should be Done Regarding Increasing Population?

   c．When Can Nature Change Urbanites?

   d．Where Can We Live as Urbanites?

精 読問題 もう一度英文を読んで、次の問いに答えなさい。

2．下線部(1)は具体的にはどういうことか。最も適切なものを選びなさい。　　　　　（3点）

   a．China will become fully urban in 2030.

   b．More than half of human beings lived in urban areas in 2008.

   c．Most of us will move to urban areas in the next thirty years.

   d．There have already been 590 million urbanites just in India.

3．下線部(2)について、田舎に暮らす人よりも都会に暮らす人のほうがよりよい経験ができるとしているものはどのようなものか。日本語で説明しなさい。　　　　　　　　　　　（5点）

_____

4．下線部(3)のノルウェーネズミについて、どのような状況下で何が起こったか。与えられた書き出しに続いて日本語で説明しなさい。　　　　　　　　　　　（5点）

   ノルウェーネズミは _____

5．下線部(4)について、the brain's amygdala と the perigenual anterior cingulate cortex とはそれぞれどのようなものか。日本語で説明しなさい。　　　　　　　　　　　（各5点）

   the brain's amygdala: _____

   the perigenual anterior cingulate cortex: _____

6．下線部(5)について本文の内容と一致しないものを一つ選びなさい。　　　　　　　（5点）

   a．If we have natural surroundings around us, we will receive mental and psychological benefit from them.

   b．We all need some natural places to go in the city which are clean, quiet, and safe.

   c．We should always make a visit to natural areas that are far from us.

   d．We should know more about how to make schools, hospitals, workplaces, and neighborhoods attractive by planting trees or flowers.

7．**全体把握** 本文の内容と合っているものをすべて選びなさい。　　　　　　　（5点）

   a．China and Liberia are half urban.

   b．Income per person per year in Kinshasa is over $250.

   c．Harvard economist Ed Glaeser insists we should make more cities like Kinshasa.

   d．Urban living affects the fear center in our brain and a main region for controlling fear and stress.

   e．Even short exposures to nature can make us more aggressive.

Lesson 12

Grammar & Usage　目標➡ 7分

1 次の会話の ☐ に入れるのに最も適当なものを選びなさい。　　　　　（各4点）

1. *A :* I'm so sorry to be late.

   B : ☐　　The meeting hasn't started yet.

   A : I'm glad to hear that.

   a．That's a pity.　　　b．That's all right.　　c．You're too late.　　d．You're welcome.

2. *A :* Now, I'd like to say a little more about our plans.

   B : ☐

   A : Sure, go ahead.　What would you like to know?

   a．Excuse me.　Could you speak up, please?

   b．I'm sorry to interrupt, but may I ask a question?

   c．I'm sorry, but could you repeat that, please?

   d．Please excuse me.　Is it all right if I leave now?

3. *A :* What did you think of the movie?

   B : ☐

   A : Me neither.

   a．Actually, I didn't really enjoy it.　　　b．To be honest, I hated it.

   c．To tell the truth, it wasn't very good.　　d．Well, I really loved it.

4. *A :* Hello, Kazuko.　What can I do for you?

   B : I was wondering if we could meet earlier than we planned, maybe on the 27th.

   A : ☐

   B : But I really need to see you before that.

   a．Can I ask you why?　　　　　　　b．Oh, I'll be away until the 29th.

   c．OK.　I've got time right now.　　　d．What time are you thinking of?

Writing　目標➡ 3分

2 1、2は（　　）内の語句を並べかえなさい。3、4は英訳しなさい。　（1、2：各3点／3、4：各6点）

1. I don't believe you.　You could (finished / have / not / soon / so / work / your).　〈立教大〉

　_____

2. Science would make (much less progress / the computer networks / to exchange / used by many scientists / without) ideas.

　_____

3. コートを着ていたら、そんなに濡れずに済んだのに。　　　　　　　　　　　　〈学習院大〉

　If you had been _____ so wet.

4. 音楽がなかったならば、私の子供時代はずっと味気ないものになっていただろう。　〈青山学院大〉

　_____

CAN-DO List　☐ 🔍 〈知識・技能〉ランダムに配列された文法・語法に関する問題に答えることができる。

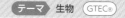

Listening 目標➡5分 テーマ 生物 GTEC® 🔊 30

3 英文を聞き、問いの答えとして最も適当なものを一つずつ選びなさい。英文の前に Situation が読み上げられます。 (各5点)

Situation: You will listen to an environmental biology professor introducing a new topic to his class.

1. What is most likely to be the main theme of this lecture?
   ① Differences between researchers in Britain and in Japan.
   ② How foreign species influence native species.
   ③ How much food ladybird beetles in Japan need to eat.
   ④ How to find articles on ladybird beetles in Japan.

2. Which of the following is true about ladybird beetles?
   ① A foreign species in Japan does not eat native species.
   ② Exotic species kill other native species when they do not have enough food.
   ③ Seven species are quickly invading other species in Britain.
   ④ The harlequin ladybird is one of the native species in Britain.

Rapid Reading 目標➡5分 テーマ 生物 GTEC®

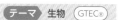

4 英文を読んで、問いの答えとして最も適当なものを一つずつ選びなさい。 (各5点)

　People have always been interested in bees.　This interest may have begun with the honey bees make.　In fact, <u>archaeologists</u> have found evidence that people have been eating honey for many thousands of years.　In the more recent past, people were interested in the way bees made honey.　They admired the way bees seemed to work so hard.　Some languages even developed expressions about people working like bees.　In English, for example, we talk about a "busy bee."　Now scientists have a new reason to be interested in bees.　They have discovered that bees are able to communicate with each other.　Research has revealed some surprising facts about this, but there are still many mysteries.

1. What does the underlined word "archaeologists" mean?
   ① scientists who study ancient societies by examining what remains of their buildings, tools, etc.
   ② scientists who study human societies and social behavior
   ③ scientists who study the materials (rocks, soils, etc.) which make up the Earth
   ④ scientists who study the relationships between living things and their surroundings

2. What is this paragraph about?
   ① expressions about bees in the English language
   ② how bees communicate with each other
   ③ people's interest in bees　　　　　　　④ the mysteries of bees

Reading

目標➡20分　　　　　　　　　　　　　　　　　テーマ　生物　　🔊 31

速 読問題 次の英文を 3 分で読んで、1. の問いに答えなさい。

All across the United States, honeybees are flying away from their hives and dying.　The disappearance of so many bees is causing a lot of worry about some important food crops.

Bees give us a lot more than delicious honey.　They are (1)pollinators——they enable plants to produce the fruits and nuts we enjoy by carrying *pollen from one plant or flower to the
5 next.　The wind pollinates oats, corn, and wheat, but many other plants (like apple trees and melon vines) depend on animals such as insects, bats, and birds.　Animals pollinate about one out of every three bites of food we eat.　In the U.S., millions of bees kept by human beekeepers fly around doing a lot of this important work for food crops.

Professional beekeepers raise honeybees, box them up, and send them on trucks to fields
10 where farmers grow food.　Bees live in groups of about 40,000 individuals called colonies. California's almond crop alone depends on about half the bees in the country, about 1.5 million colonies!　The bees pollinate the almond *groves for about six weeks, and then are sent on to work other crops.　But now the almond crop and many others could be in trouble with so many bees dying.

15 Researchers at government and university laboratories all over the country are trying to figure out why so many bee colonies are dying.　However, (2)bees are hard to study, according to Dr. Jeff Pettis of the Bee Research Laboratory at the U.S. Agricultural Research Service. Most bees die away from the hive, so researchers don't have dead bodies to examine.　Also, when researchers return to a hive after two weeks, about half the bees they studied on their
20 first visit will be dead, replaced by new ones in the natural life cycle of bees.　What makes their research even harder is that these busy insects fly up to two miles away from their hive in search of pollen and *nectar from flowers.　So when bees pick up diseases or get exposed to poisons in their environment, it is hard to know exactly where (3)that happened.

Researchers do have some ideas about (4)what could be affecting bee health.　Bees could be
25 sick from poisons widely used to kill insects, or they might not be getting enough good food to stay healthy.　Also, tiny creatures called mites feed on bees.　"Any or all of these things could be weakening the honey bees," explains Pettis, "and then a virus or bacteria could be doing the killing."

Pettis is hoping for a solution, because bees are so important.　"You can eat plain *oatmeal every day and get by, as oats are pollinated by the wind," he says.   "But if you want to add 30

some blueberries or nuts to your daily oatmeal, those are the things you have to thank

pollinators for.   Bees are worth protecting because their work adds so much to the diversity

of our meals."

(490 words / 武蔵大)

---

⁴ pollen[pá(ː)lən]：花粉　　¹² grove[gróυv]：果樹園　　²² nectar[néktər]：(花の)蜜
²⁹ oatmeal[óυtmìːl]：オートミール(朝食によく出される、牛乳と砂糖をオートムギに混ぜて作ったかゆ)

1．この英文は全体として何について述べていますか。一つ選びなさい。 (5点)
  a．The decrease in the number of honeybees and the crisis of fruit production.
  b．The difficulty in studying lifestyles of honeybees.
  c．The reason for decreasing honeybees and countermeasures for it.
  d．The role honeybees play in pollinating flowers.

精 読問題 もう一度英文を読んで、次の問いに答えなさい。
2．下線部(1)の pollinators の働きを、本文に則して日本語で説明しなさい。 (7点)

3．第3パラグラフの内容と合っているものを一つ選びなさい。 (3点)
  a．Bees are raised in boxes on trucks in the U.S.
  b．California's almond crop needs about 20,000 bees.
  c．Farmers raise bees for their crops in California.
  d．There are about 3 million colonies of bees in the U.S.

4．下線部(2)について、理由を三つ、日本語で説明しなさい。 (各4点)
  ・
  ・
  ・

5．下線部(3)が指すものを、具体的に日本語で説明しなさい。 (7点)

6．下線部(4)の例として挙げられているものをすべて選びなさい。 (4点)
  a．Climate change
  b．Deforestation
  c．Lack of proper food
  d．Tiny creatures which do harm to the bodies of honeybees.
  e．The destruction of hives by small animals
  f．The use of insecticides

7．全体把握 本文の内容と合っているものをすべて選びなさい。 (8点)
  a．Bees are to apple trees what the wind is to wheat.
  b．A dramatic increase in the number of bees is causing trouble for farmers.
  c．Bees often travel far from their hives and live for many months.
  d．Bees produce the honey that helps plants bear fruits or nuts.
  e．Pettis thinks the bee problem will be solved quickly and easily.
  f．The activities of bees contribute to the variety of what we eat.

Lesson 13

1 次の各文の □ に入れるのに最も適当なものを選びなさい。　　　　　　　（各2点）

1. If I buy a second-hand computer, it will □ me hundreds of dollars.
    a. add　　　　　　b. help　　　　　　c. keep　　　　　　d. save

2. Flight 702 □ into the Persian Gulf, killing everyone aboard.　〈慶應義塾大〉
    a. clashed　　　　b. collided　　　　c. crashed　　　　d. struck

3. Do you think this blouse □ my red skirt?　　　　　　　　　〈上智大〉
    a. goes with　　　b. goes on　　　　c. takes on　　　　d. takes after

4. I'll have read through this magazine by the time I □ you again.　〈関西学院大〉
    a. see　　　　　　b. saw　　　　　　c. will see　　　　d. had seen

5. You seem to be good friends with Lucy.　How long □ her?　〈学習院大〉
    a. do you know　　　　　　　　　　b. had you known
    c. have you been knowing　　　　　d. have you known

6. You had better have that tooth □ out.　　　　　　　　　　〈立命館大〉
    a. to pull　　　　b. pull　　　　　　c. pulled　　　　　d. pulling

2 次の各文の下線部とほぼ同じ意味を表すものを選びなさい。　　　　　　（各3点）

1. She made believe that she had not understood anything.　〈関西外国語大〉
    a. tried　　　　　b. was careful　　　c. deceived　　　d. pretended

2. She felt ill at ease since she was the only person that couldn't speak English.〈神戸学院大〉
    a. enthusiastic　　b. glad　　　　　c. satisfied　　　d. uncomfortable

3. It was sensible of you to lock the door.　　　　　　　　　〈関西外国語大〉
    a. sensitive　　　b. reasonable　　　c. intellectual　　d. sympathetic

4. I don't like students who don't come to the class on time.　〈立命館大〉
    a. lately　　　　　b. regularly　　　c. timely　　　　d. punctually

3 1、2は（　　）内の語句を並べかえなさい。3は英訳しなさい。　（1、2：各3点／3：6点）

1. この車は私が2年前に買って以来故障ばかりしている。　　　　〈名古屋外国語大〉
   (me / but / has / this car / problems / nothing / caused) since I bought it two years ago.

   _____

2. You are advised to (full / of / English / to / chance / use / speak / every / make).
   　　　　　　　　　　　　　　　　　　　　　　　　　　　　　　〈静岡県立大〉

   _____

3. あなたが助けてくださっていれば、私はその仕事を終えられましたのに。　〈高知大〉
   With _____ .

4 対話と質問を聞き、その答えとして最も適当なものを一つずつ選びなさい。 (各5点)

1. ① Bacon, eggs, sausages, tomato, tea, toast, muffins, marmalade.
   ② Bacon, scrambled eggs, sausages, tomato, tea, mushrooms, marmalade.
   ③ Orange juice, bacon, fried eggs, sausages, tomato, mushrooms, tea, muffins, marmalade.
   ④ Orange juice, fried eggs, sausages, tomato, tea, toast, marmalade.

2. ① A tea, a cake, a sandwich, a hamburger, a vanilla ice cream, a chocolate brownie.
   ② A tea, a hamburger, a chocolate brownie.
   ③ A tea, a hamburger, a vanilla ice cream, a chocolate brownie.
   ④ A tea, a sandwich, a hamburger, a vanilla ice cream, a chocolate brownie.

Rapid Reading 目標➡5分 テーマ コーヒーショップの求人 GTEC®

5 掲示を読み取って、問いに対する答えとして最も適当なものを一つずつ選びなさい。 (各5点)

PART-TIME WORKERS NEEDED

Sunrise Coffee Shop is looking for part-time employees for our Station Road Branch, due to open at the beginning of June.

・Our shop hours are from 7 a.m. to 23 p.m., every day.

・Hours are flexible but workers who can commit to at least 20 hours a week are preferred. We employ university students, but application is limited to students aged 19 and over. In the case of students, it is possible to work a maximum of 10 hours a week.

・The job description includes waiting on tables, working at the cash register and doing the dishes.

・Starting pay is the prefectural minimum (excluding transport expense), with regular raises based on performance and time worked.

Staff members are required to wear the uniform (that is lent to employees). Shoes must always be worn; sandals are prohibited. Men must wear a white shirt with collar and tie. Women should wear a white blouse or shirt. Long hair must be tied back.

Email: parttime@seekmail.com with your name and contact details to arrange an interview.

---

1. Which of the following statements is true?
   ① The Station Road Branch of Sunrise Coffee Shop has already been in operation.
   ② Sunrise Coffee Shop is not going to hire high school students.
   ③ Sunrise Coffee Shop is not open on weekends.
   ④ The employer doesn't care about anything else as long as waitpersons wear the uniform.

2. Which of the following statements is best supported by the above recruitment guide?
   ① Part-timer's working hours don't take the students into consideration.
   ② Sunrise Coffee Shop adopts a pay system based on seniority.
   ③ Sunrise Coffee Shop takes care of employees' appearance.
   ④ Sunrise Coffee Shop would like to hire a waitress, not a waiter.

Reading 目標➡20分 テーマ 仕事 34

速読問題 次の英文を3分で読んで、1. の問いに答えなさい。

Starbucks —— like a handful of other companies —— has succeeded in teaching the kind of life skills that schools, families, and communities have failed to provide.　With more than 137,000 current employees and more than one million *alumni, (1)Starbucks is now, in a sense, one of the nation's largest educators.　All of those employees, in their first year alone, spent at

5　least fifty hours in Starbucks' classrooms, and dozens more at home with Starbucks' workbooks and talking to the Starbucks' *mentors assigned to them.

At the core of that education is an intense focus on an all-important habit: (2)willpower. Dozens of studies show that willpower is the single most important keystone habit for individual success.　In a 2005 study, for instance, researchers from the University of

10　Pennsylvania analyzed 164 eighth-grade students, measuring their IQs and other factors, including how much willpower the students demonstrated, as measured by tests of their self-discipline.

Students who used high levels of willpower were more likely to earn higher grades in their classes and gain admission into more selective schools.　They had fewer absences and spent

15　less time watching television and more hours on homework.　"Highly self-disciplined students *outperformed in every subject," the researchers wrote.　"Self-discipline predicted academic performance better than did IQ.　Self-discipline also predicted which students would improve their grades over the course of the school year, whereas IQ did not.　Self-discipline has a bigger effect on academic performance than does intellectual talent."

20　And the best way to strengthen willpower and *give students a leg up, studies show, is to (3)make it into a habit.　"Sometimes it looks like people with great self-control aren't working hard —— but that's because they've made it automatic," one of the University of Pennsylvania researchers told me.　"Their willpower occurs without them having to think about it."

25　For Starbucks, willpower is more than an academic curiosity.　When the company began *plotting its great growth strategy in the late 1990s, executives recognized that success required *cultivating (4)an environment that justified paying four dollars for a fancy cup of coffee.　The company needed to train its employees to deliver a bit of joy alongside *lattes and *scones.　So early on, Starbucks started researching how they could teach employees to

regulate their emotions and have the self-discipline to deliver a burst of *pep with every 30
serving.　Unless employees are trained to put aside their personal problems, their emotions
will inevitably spill into how they treat customers.　However, if a worker knows how to
remain focused and disciplined, even at the end of an eight-hour shift, they'll deliver the
higher class of fast food service that Starbucks customers expect.

　The company spent millions of dollars developing curriculums to train employees on self- 35
discipline.　Executives wrote workbooks that, in effect, serve as guides to how to make
willpower a habit in worker's lives.　Those curriculums are, in part, why Starbucks has
grown from a sleepy Seattle company into (5)a behemoth with more than seventeen thousand
stores and *revenues of more than $10 billion a year.　　　　　　(503 words / 日本大)

---

³alumni[əlʌ́mnaɪ]：旧従業員　　⁶mentor[méntɔːr]：社員教育係
¹⁶outperform[àʊtpərfɔ́ːrm]：よりよい成績を上げる　　²⁰give ... a leg up：…の成功を手助けする
²⁶plot[plɑ́(ː)t]：…を計画する　　²⁷cultivate[kʌ́ltɪvèɪt]：…を作り出す
²⁸latte[lɑ́ːteɪ]：ミルクを入れたエスプレッソ・コーヒー　　²⁹scone[skóʊn]：ビスケット
³⁰pep[pép]：元気　　³⁹revenue[révənjùː]：総収入

1．この英文のタイトルとして最も適当なものを、一つ選びなさい。　　　　　（5点）
　　a．The company policy of Starbucks ── Customer-first
　　b．The company policy of Starbucks ── Every employee counts
　　c．The employee education of Starbucks ── Education in schools and offices
　　d．The employee education of Starbucks ── Self-discipline

精 読問題 もう一度英文を読んで、次の問いに答えなさい。
2．下線部(1)で筆者は何を言おうとしているか、一つ選びなさい。　　　　　（5点）
　　a．More than one million people comes to Starbucks in a year.
　　b．More than one million people have been educated in Starbucks.
　　c．Starbucks has a lot of coffee houses in many countries.
　　d．Starbucks has its own philosophy about coffee.
3．下線部(2)とほぼ同じ意味で使われている語を、第3・第4パラグラフからそれぞれ一つずつ抜き出しなさい。
　　　　　　　　　　　　　　　　　　　　　　　　　　　　　　　　　　　（各6点）

　　第3パラグラフ：(　　　　　　　)　　　第4パラグラフ：(　　　　　　　)
4．下線部(3)の具体的な内容を、日本語で説明しなさい。　　　　　　　　　（7点）
　　_____
5．下線部(4)とほぼ同じ意味で使われている表現を、同じパラグラフから抜き出しなさい。　（7点）
　　_____
6．下線部(5)について、スターバックスが大企業に成長できた理由を70字程度の日本語で説明しなさい。　（8点）

Lesson 13　55

Lesson 14

Grammar & Usage　目標➡5分

1▶ 次の各文の ☐ に入れるのに最も適当なものを選びなさい。　　　　　　　　（各2点）

1. Some people are unable to take advantage of opportunities ☐ making mistakes.
   a. for fear of　　　b. but for　　　c. in need of　　　d. as for

2. If you have any questions or concerns about your trip abroad, please don't ☐ to ask me.　　〈関西学院大〉
   a. refuse　　　b. cease　　　c. afford　　　d. hesitate

3. Everybody suffers from colds ☐ some extent.　　〈上智大〉
   a. on　　　b. to　　　c. at　　　d. with

4. When it ☐ to classical music, very few people know more than Jane.　　〈日本女子大〉
   a. brings　　　b. comes　　　c. gets　　　d. goes

5. At first we didn't like each other, but in the ☐ we became good friends.　　〈南山大〉
   a. end　　　b. minute　　　c. moment　　　d. term

6. She speaks French, to say ☐ of English.　　〈青山学院大〉
   a. anything　　　b. something　　　c. everything　　　d. nothing

7. I like him ☐ the more on account of his honesty.　　〈成蹊大〉
   a. for　　　b. just　　　c. none　　　d. all

Writing　目標➡5分

2▶ 1、2は（　　）内の語句を並べかえなさい。3、4は英訳しなさい。　（1、2：各3点／3、4：各6点）

1. World War I ended in 1918.　It was a very bad war.　Many Europeans believed there would be no more wars.　They called World War I "(all / end / the war / to / wars)."

2. Environmental groups have organized a march (against / a road / government plans / to build / to protest) through the forest.

3. 東京への飛行機で出会った男性が親切にも私たちのガイドをしてくれました。
   The man _____.

4. 日本では、数字の4を表す語は死を意味する語のように聞こえるので、不吉だとみなされている。
   In Japan, _____ so it is considered unlucky.

3 英語の授業での3人による会話を聞き、問いの答えとして最も適当なものを一つずつ選びなさい。

（各5点）

1. Which of the following is NOT a course mentioned in the conversation?
   ① "Cognitive Neuroscience" at the University of Essex.
   ② "English Language Teaching" at the University of Essex.
   ③ "Psycholinguistics" at the University of Essex.
   ④ "Psychology of Early Development" at the University of Reading.

2. Which of the following is likely to be true?
   ① Both female students are interested in foreign language learning.
   ② Koji wants to be an English teacher.
   ③ Two female students will apply to the same university.
   ④ Two of them will study how people learn something in the brain.

Rapid Reading | 目標➡5分 | テーマ 心理 英検®

4 問いの ☐ に入れるのに最も適当なものを一つずつ選びなさい。 （各5点）

　In an experiment, a display booth was set up in a California supermarket, offering customers the opportunity to taste some new jams.　Every hour the format of their display was changed. One hour there would be lots of choices: 24 different kinds of jam.　The next hour the choices would be much reduced: just 6 kinds of jam.　Over the course of ten hours of total observation, 754 shoppers were *tracked.　Twenty-four kinds of jam attracted more customers to take a look (60%) than just 6 choices (40%).　However, of those who stopped to try out some jam, only 3% bought jam when selecting from 24 kinds of jam, whereas 30%——ten times as many! —— bought jam after *sampling from 6 kinds.　Giving customers more choices actually reduced sales.

---

⁵track[trǽk]：…を調査の対象とする　　⁸sample[sǽmp(ə)l]：…を試食する

1. In the experiment, the display with 6 kinds of jam ☐ .
   ① attracted more customers than the display with 24 kinds of jam
   ② attracted 30% of all 754 shoppers
   ③ resulted in sales to 70% of all 754 shoppers
   ④ resulted in more sales than the display with 24 kinds of jam

2. The most appropriate title for this passage is ☐
   ① How Much Choice Do Customers Want?
   ② How to Please Customers in Supermarkets.
   ③ More Choice Is Better.
   ④ The Decision-Making Process of American Consumers.

Reading 目標➡20分 ////////////////// テーマ 心理 🔊 36

速読問題 次の英文を3分で読んで、1. の問いに答えなさい。

Choices

Last year, I went to the store to buy a pair of jeans. I tend to wear my jeans until they're falling apart, so it had been a while since my last purchase. A nice young saleswoman greeted me.

5 "I want a pair of jeans——size 32-28," I said.

"Do you want them slim-fit, easy-fit or relaxed-fit?" she replied. "Do you want them looking new or already worn? Do you want them with a button front or a zipper?"

I was so shocked that I didn't know what to say. I finally said something like, "I just want regular jeans. You know, the kind that used to be the only kind."

10 The trouble was that (1)there was no such thing as "regular jeans" anymore. Besides, with all these options before me, I was no longer sure that I wanted "regular" ones. Perhaps the easy-fit or relaxed-fit would be more comfortable. So I decided to try them all.

The jeans I bought turned out to be just fine, but what occurred to me on that day is that buying a pair of jeans shouldn't be a day-long project.

15 By creating all these options, the industry undoubtedly has done a favor for customers with varied tastes and body types. However, it has also created (2)a new problem. In the past, a buyer like me might have had to settle for a fit that was not perfect, but at least purchasing jeans was a five-minute affair. Now, it has become a complex decision in which I was forced to invest time, energy, and no small amount of self-doubt and anxiety.

20 It's not just jeans——forty-five types of bread, sixty-two kinds of drinks, eighty-three models of mobile telephones and dozens of calling plans. The list goes on. Wherever we turn, we face a huge range of choices.

The good side of having all these choices is obvious. Choice equals freedom, and in a democratic society, freedom is among our most dearly held values. Economists tell us there 25 can never be too much choice. If you don't care about the variety in telephones, you can always just ignore it. But if you do care, variety means that you ought to be able to find the phone that is just right for you.

Convincing as this might sound, however, there's growing evidence that this logic is mistaken. For many of us, increased choice means decreased satisfaction. The fact that 30 some choice is good doesn't necessarily mean that more choice is better. There's a cost. Too

CAN-DO List ☐ 🔘 〈思考力・判断力・表現力〉「心理」をテーマとした英文の展開を的確に理解することができる。

many options can paralyze, not free you.　Studies show, for example, that as a store increases the varieties of chocolates on its shelves, (3)shoppers are more likely to leave without buying any product at all.

　　The more choices we have, the more we seem to regret the decisions we make.　Greater options seem to raise our expectations.　So, we wonder: "Did we get what we wanted? 35 Could another of the alternatives have been better?"　While it may be true that a life without any freedom of choice would not be worth living, more choice doesn't necessarily mean greater happiness.

(521 words / 京都産業大)

1. 筆者が最も言いたいことを、一つ選びなさい。　　　　　　　　　　　　　　（7点）
　　a. Life without the freedom of choice is not worth living.
　　b. More choices do not always bring more happiness.
　　c. The fewer choices there are, the better it is.
　　d. The more choices there are, the better it is.

精 読問題 もう一度英文を読んで、次の問いに答えなさい。

2. 下線部(1)について、筆者にとって regular jeans がなかったというのはなぜか。日本語で説明しなさい。　（7点）
_____

3. 下線部(2)の具体的な内容を日本語で説明しなさい。　　　　　　　　　　（7点）
_____
_____

4. 下線部(3)の理由はどのようなことだと考えられるか。日本語で説明しなさい。　（7点）
_____

5. **全体把握** □ に入れるのに最も適当なものを、一つずつ選びなさい。　（各4点）
　(1) The author usually buy new jeans □ .
　　a. that are more comfortable than "regular" ones
　　b. when his old ones are worn out　　　　c. which are worn out
　(2) The author was "shocked" in the jeans shop because □ .
　　a. he was not able to find a pair of jeans that he liked
　　b. the shop had no jeans with a button front or a zipper
　　c. there were so many different kinds of jeans to choose from
　(3) Today, shopping for jeans □ .
　　a. helps the industry create more options
　　b. is impossible for people like the author　　c. takes more time than before
　(4) A great variety of options to choose from is □ .
　　a. more important for mobile phones than for jeans
　　b. not such a good things as it might seem　　c. not recognized in economics
　(5) A store will probably sell more chocolates if it □ .
　　a. increases choice　　　　b. increases shelves　　　　c. limits choice

Grammar & Usage 　目標➡ 7分

1 次の各文の（A）と（B）に入れるのに最も適当な組み合わせを選びなさい。　　　　　（各4点）

1. I need a bigger refrigerator, but I'll have to (A) without a new one (B) I can afford it.
   - a．A : do 　　　　B : until
   - b．A : do 　　　　B : when
   - c．A : keep 　　　B : until
   - d．A : keep 　　　B : when

2. Wood (A) be used as the main fuel, but nowadays fossil fuels (B) widely.
   - a．A : used to 　　　　B : are used
   - b．A : used to 　　　　B : have been used
   - c．A : was used to 　　B : are used
   - d．A : was used to 　　B : have been used

3. In advertising, it's hard to come up (A) clever (B) to attract consumers.
   - a．A : on 　　　B : propaganda
   - b．A : on 　　　B : slogans
   - c．A : with 　　B : propaganda
   - d．A : with 　　B : slogans

4. The Internet has become (A) powerful a tool (B) people living anywhere can access any educational resource.
   - a．A : so 　　　B : but
   - b．A : so 　　　B : that
   - c．A : such 　　B : but
   - d．A : such 　　B : that

5. (A) so considerate (B) him to come and see his grandmother in the hospital every day.
   - a．A : He is 　　B : for
   - b．A : He is 　　B : of
   - c．A : It is 　　B : for
   - d．A : It is 　　B : of

6. The (A) of treatment at the hospital is much lower for (B) who have health insurance.
   - a．A : cost 　　B : them
   - b．A : cost 　　B : those
   - c．A : fare 　　B : them
   - d．A : fare 　　B : those

Writing 　目標➡ 3分

2 1、2は（　　）内の語を並べかえなさい。3、4は英訳しなさい。　　（1、2：各3点／3、4：各6点）

1. I don't know what it is, (about / but / her / is / mysterious / something / there).〈立教大〉

   _____

2. I'll lend you this book, but (back / before / get / I / it / make / sure) the end of the week.
   〈立教大〉

   _____

3. 天気予報によると雨は明朝にはやむとのことです。　　　　　　　　〈学習院大〉

   According _____ .

4. 私は高校生のころ、バス通学でした。　　　　　　　　　　　　　〈大阪女子大〉

   _____

CAN-DO List 　□ 　〈知識・技能〉ランダムに配列された文法・語法に関する問題に答えることができる。

3 英文を聞き、問いの答えとして最も適当なものを一つずつ選びなさい。 (各5点)

1. What does the professor think is important in our life?

① Completing the four-year degree course. ② Continuing learning.

③ Gaining "must-have" things. ④ Making very important decisions.

2. Which of the following is true about what the professor says?

① Having inner strength is more important than being modest.

② It is possible to make an overnight success.

③ "Must-have" items help us in our consumer society.

④ We need to prepare to make our dreams come true.

Rapid Reading 目標➡5分 テーマ 社会の変化

4 記事を読み取って、問いに対する答えとして最も適当なものを一つずつ選びなさい。 (各5点)

A Judicial Reform May 21, 2014

On May 21, 2004, "A law concerning criminal trials in which *saiban-in* (citizen judges) participated" passed the Upper House. 5 years later, on May 21, 2009, the *saiban-in* system came into effect. Japan's postwar judicial system was headed for a new era of participatory adjudication.

In Japan, from 1928 to 1943, a jury system based on the Anglo-American model was used in criminal trials. However, it was abolished in the era of militarism because such a democratic system would have been inconvenient for the government at that time. So, in a trial, before the *saiban-in* system was introduced, three professional judges would have made the decision. It is said that the new system is similar to the French and German system of "trial by consultation." Under this system, judges and citizens work together in deciding major felony cases, such as those involving murder.

At present, each case is decided by a panel of three judges and six citizens. Lay judges deliberate cases in a joint session with professional judges, ( ). This panel decides "guilty" or "not guilty" and if it decides "guilty," it also decides the level of punishment, including the death penalty. Each member of the panel has one vote. A decision is made by a majority vote that includes at least one professional ballot.

Citizen judges are randomly selected from eligible voters. It is said that one of every 120 or so citizens will serve as a lay judge in his or her lifetime. Next year, you may be selected!

1. A phrase is missing in ( ). Select the best answer to complete the text.

① declaring the judgment ② detecting who is the criminal

③ exchanging opinions ④ mustering *saiban-in*

2. Which of the following statements is true?

① In Japan, we hadn't had a system similar to the *saiban-in* system before 2014.

② It is possible that the panel will sentence the accused to death.

③ There are no restrictions on the majority vote in deciding the judgment.

④ All Japanese people have the possibility of being selected as *saiban-in* every year.

 □ 🎧 〈思考力・判断力・表現力〉「スピーチ」の内容を聞き取り、理解することができる。 **Lesson 15** 61

□ 📖 〈思考力・判断力・表現力〉「社会の変化の記事」を読んで、概要を把握できる。

Reading　目標➡20分 　　　　　　　　　　　　　テーマ　変化　🔊 38

速読問題 次の英文を３分で読んで、１. の問いに答えなさい。

Everything changes.　Our body changes.　Our ideas change and so do our moods, or the moods of the people we are close to.　Our loves and our friendships change.　Our finances and our life plans change.　The causes of our suffering or happiness change.　The political situation changes.　Fashion and the weather change.　Even change itself changes.

5　In a universe in which nothing stays the same, (1)it is hard to find any safe place which may offer us protection and security.　The only way to survive consists in the art of adjusting to events that continually take us by surprise.　If you adjust, you survive.　If, in the midst of changing conditions, you stay fixed, you die.

I am a psychologist.　The work of my profession can be defined as the recovery, or the
10　learning, of flexibility.　We help people who are suffering from mental or emotional diseases because they are still facing today's situations with yesterday's strategies.　Someone who was abused as a child, for example, lives in a constant tension, perhaps closing himself to others like a frightened child.　Or else, becoming a slave, he tries to win favor with a potential enemy.　(2)These attitudes, although they may have been sufficient in the past, have no more
15　meaning today.　Now the danger is over, and the time has come to stop pretending and start living.　Another example: a parent has devoted many years to the care of children, looked after their health, listened to their dreams and their troubles, and given her heart and soul to their well-being.　The children grow up, leave home, and (3)all this work and care has to stop ——like an ancient machine that is not useful anymore and is left rusting in a corner.

20　The idea is to help all of us (4)recognize present reality.　Because, however hard it may be, reality is our great teacher.　Reality proceeds of its own accord, without considering our hopes and dreams.　Our fantasies are idle if they do not help us face life as it is in this very moment.

That is why flexibility is not just a successful strategy.　It is also a spiritual quality.　It
25　suggests freedom from attachments, consciousness in the present, and acceptance of what is. Changes in our life can be unpleasant, even terrible: the people we love may not love us as before; our professional ability is failing; our body is weakening; our products are no longer selling as they used to; friends who used to give us warmth and support have forgotten us; the activities that once excited us now seem boring and empty.

In the face of constant change, as (5)a Chinese philosopher once suggested, we should be as 30
fluid as water, which flows over and around rocks, changing its shape to flow on.   If we can let
go of the beliefs we are most fond of, then we can open ourselves to the new, to paradox and
mystery.   This is creativity.   This attitude becomes a way of life, even a spiritual path.   We
are able to let go of old models, and become humble enough to start all over again.

(524 words / 静岡大学)

1. この英文は全体として何について述べていますか。一つ選びなさい。　　　　　　　　　（5点）
　　a. The importance of accepting changes and adjusting to the trends.
　　b. The importance of flexibility and accepting changes.
　　c. The importance of staying fixed and not being influenced by others.
　　d. What changes and what does not change with the times.

精 読問題 もう一度英文を読んで、次の問いに答えなさい。

2. 下線部(1)について、筆者は解決策としてどのようなことを提示しているか。それが最も現れている語をこのパラグラフから一語で抜き出しなさい。　　　　　　　　　　　　　　　（4点）
　　(　　　　　　　　)

3. 下線部(2)の具体的な内容を、日本語で二つ説明しなさい。　　　　　　　　　　　　　（各3点）
　　・_____
　　・_____

4. 下線部(3)の具体的な内容を、日本語で三つ説明しなさい。　　　　　　　　　　　　　（各2点）
　　・_____
　　・_____
　　・_____

5. 下線部(4)とほぼ同じ内容を表している表現を、第4パラグラフから抜き出しなさい。　（4点）
　　_____

6. 下線部(5)の「中国の賢人」が言ったことを、日本語で説明しなさい。　　　　　　　　（5点）
　　_____

7. 全体把握 本文の内容と合っているものをすべて選びなさい。　　　　　　　　　　　　（8点）
　　a. There are some things which stay fixed all the time in the vast universe.
　　b. The writer is a psychologist who helps people suffering from mental or emotional
　　　　diseases.
　　c. Abused children always try to escape from their potential enemies.
　　d. Some people don't like changes and don't want to accept them right away.
　　e. "We should be as fluid as water" means that we should stick to one philosophy all the
　　　　time.

Sources

■Listening

Lesson 6（グラフ）

熱帯林の年平均減少面積（『世界の統計』2009年度版）

■Rapid Reading

Lesson 6（グラフ）

温室効果ガスの温暖化への影響度（オークリッジ国立研究所資料）

二酸化炭素排出国（オークリッジ国立研究所資料）

主な国の二酸化炭素排出量の推移（オークリッジ国立研究所資料）

Lesson 12

MIKULECKY, BEATRICE S.；JEFFRIES, LINDA, MORE READING POWER, 1st Ed.,

©1996. Reprinted by permission of Pearson Education, Inc., New York, New York.

■Reading

Lesson 2

The Japan Times（2019年5月26日掲載）（一部改変）

Lesson 13

Excerpts from THE POWER OF HABIT：WHY WE DO WHAT WE DO IN LIFE AND BUSINESS by Charles Duhigg, copyright ©2012 by Charles Duhigg. Used by permission of Random House, an imprint and division of Penguin Random House LLC. All rights reserved.

Lesson 15

"Flexibility" from THE POWER OF KINDNESS：THE UNEXPECTED BENEFITS OF LEADING A COMPASSIONATE LIFE by Piero Ferrucci, foreword by the Dalai Lama, translated by Vivian Reid Ferrucci, copyright ©2006 by Piero Ferrucci. Translation ©2006 by Vivian Reid Ferrucci. Used by permission of Tarcher, an imprint of Penguin Publishing Group, a division of Penguin Random House LLC. All rights reserved.